THE KIPLING READER

SELECTIONS FROM THE BOOKS OF RUDYARD KIPLING

NEW AND REVISED EDITION

MACMILLAN AND CO., LIMITED
ST. MARTIN'S STREET LONDON

1937

First Edition 1900.
Reprinted with corrections 1901.
Reprinted 1907, 1908, 1910, 1912, 1914, 1916, 1918 (twice), 1919 (twice), 1920, 1921, 1923 (twice), 1924, 1925, 1927, 1930, 1932, 1936, 1937.

PRINTED IN GREAT BRITAIN

CONTENTS

PROSE

POETRY

'RIKKI-TIKKI-TAVI.'

At the hole where he went in
Red-Eye called to Wrinkle-Skin.
Hear what little Red-Eye saith:
'Nag, come up and dance with death!'

Eye to eye and head to head,
(*Keep the measure, Nag.*)
This shall end when one is dead;
(*At thy pleasure, Nag.*)
Turn for turn and twist for twist—
(*Run and hide thee, Nag.*)
Hah! The hooded Death has missed!
(*Woe betide thee, Nag!*)

THIS is the story of the great war that Rikki-tikki-tavi fought single-handed, through the bath-rooms of the big bungalow in Segowlee cantonment. Darzee, the tailor-bird, helped him, and Chuchundra, the musk-rat, who never comes out into the middle of the floor, but always creeps round by the wall, gave him advice; but Rikki-tikki did the real fighting.

He was a mongoose, rather like a little cat in his fur and his tail, but quite like a weasel in his head and habits. His eyes and the end of his restless nose were pink; he could scratch himself anywhere he pleased, with any leg, front or back, that he chose to use; he could fluff up his tail till it looked like a bottle-brush, and his war-cry, as he scuttled through the long grass, was: '*Rikk-tikk-tikki-tikki-tchk!*'

One day, a high summer flood washed him out of the burrow where he lived with his father and mother, and carried him, kicking and clucking, down a roadside ditch. He found a little wisp of grass floating there, and clung to it till he lost his senses. When he revived, he was lying in the hot sun on the middle of a garden path, very draggled indeed, and a small boy was saying: 'Here's a dead mongoose. Let's have a funeral.'

'No,' said his mother; 'let's take him in and dry him. Perhaps he isn't really dead.'

They took him into the house, and a big man picked him up between his finger and thumb, and said he was not dead but half choked; so they wrapped him in cotton-wool, and warmed him and he opened his eyes and sneezed.

'Now,' said the big man (he was an Englishman who had just moved into the bungalow); 'don't frighten him and we'll see what he'll do.'

It is the hardest thing in the world to frighten a mongoose, because he is eaten up from nose to tail with curiosity. The motto of all the mongoose family is 'Run and find out'; and Rikki-tikki was a true mongoose. He looked at the cotton-wool, decided that it was not good to eat, ran all round the table, sat up and put his fur in order, scratched himself, and jumped on the small boy's shoulder.

'Don't be frightened, Teddy,' said his father. 'That's his way of making friends.'

'Ouch! He's tickling under my chin,' said Teddy.

Rikki-tikki looked down between the boy's collar and neck, snuffed at his ear, and climbed down to the floor, where he sat rubbing his nose.

'Good gracious,' said Teddy's mother, 'and that's a wild creature! I suppose he's so tame because we've been kind to him.'

'All mongooses are like that,' said her husband. 'If Teddy doesn't pick him up by the tail, or try to put him in a cage, he'll run in and out of the house all day long. Let's give him something to eat.'

They gave him a little piece of raw meat. Rikki-tikki liked it immensely, and when it was finished he went out into the verandah and sat in the sunshine and fluffed up his fur to make it dry to the roots. Then he felt better.

'There are more things to find out about in this house,' he said to himself, 'than all my family could find out in all their lives. I shall certainly stay and find out.'

He spent all that day roaming over the house. He nearly drowned himself in the bath tubs, put his nose into the ink on a writing-table, and burnt it on the end of the big man's cigar, for he climbed up in the big man's lap to see how writing was done. At nightfall he ran into Teddy's nursery to watch how the kerosene-lamps were lighted, and when Teddy went to bed Rikki-tikki climbed up too; but he was a restless companion, because he had to get up and attend to every noise all through the night, and find out what made it. Teddy's mother and father came in, the last thing, to look at their boy, and Rikki-tikki was awake on the pillow. 'I don't like that,' said Teddy's mother; 'he may bite the child.' 'He'll do no such thing,' said the father. 'Teddy's safer with that little beast than if he had a bloodhound to watch him. If a snake came into the nursery now——'

But Teddy's mother wouldn't think of anything so awful.

Early in the morning Rikki-tikki came to early breakfast in the verandah riding on Teddy's shoulder, and they gave him banana and some boiled egg; and he sat on all their laps one after the other, because every well-brought-up mongoose always hopes to be a house-mongoose some day and have rooms to run about in, and Rikki-tikki's mother (she used to live in the General's house at Segowlee) had carefully told Rikki what to do if ever he came across white men.

Then Rikki-tikki went out into the garden to see what was to be seen. It was a large garden, only half cultivated, with bushes as big as summer-houses of Marshal Niel roses, lime and orange trees, clumps of bamboos, and thickets of high grass. Rikki-tikki licked his lips. 'This is a splendid hunting-ground,' he said, and his tail grew bottle-brushy at the thought of it, and he scuttled up and down the garden, snuffing here and there till he heard very sorrowful voices in a thorn-bush.

It was Darzee, the tailor-bird, and his wife. They had made a beautiful nest by pulling two big leaves together and stitching them up the edges with fibres, and had filled the hollow with cotton and downy fluff. The nest swayed to and fro, as they sat on the rim and cried.

'What is the matter?' asked Rikki-tikki.

'We are very miserable,' said Darzee. 'One of our babies fell out of the nest yesterday, and Nag ate him.'

'H'm!' said Rikki-tikki, 'that is very sad—but I am a stranger here. Who is Nag?'

Darzee and his wife only cowered down in the nest without answering, for from the thick grass at the foot of the bush there came a low hiss—a horrid cold sound that made Rikki-tikki jump back two clear feet. Then inch by inch out of the grass rose up the head and spread hood of Nag, the big black cobra, and he was five feet long from tongue to tail. When he had lifted one-third of himself clear of the ground, he stayed balancing to and fro exactly as a dandelion-tuft balances in the wind, and he looked at Rikki-tikki with the wicked snake's eyes that never change their expression, whatever the snake may be thinking of.

'Who is Nag?' said he. '*I* am Nag. The great god Brahm put his mark upon all our people when the first cobra spread his hood to keep the sun off Brahm as he slept. Look, and be afraid!'

He spread out his hood more than ever, and Rikki-tikki

saw the spectacle-mark on the back of it that looks exactly like the eye part of a hook-and-eye fastening. He was afraid for the minute; but it is impossible for a mongoose to stay frightened for any length of time, and though Rikki-tikki had never met a live cobra before, his mother had fed him on dead ones, and he knew that all a grown mongoose's business in life was to fight and eat snakes. Nag knew that too, and at the bottom of his cold heart he was afraid.

'Well,' said Rikki-tikki, and his tail began to fluff up again, 'marks or no marks, do you think it is right for you to eat fledglings out of a nest?'

Nag was thinking to himself, and watching the least little movement in the grass behind Rikki-tikki. He knew that mongooses in the garden meant death sooner or later for him and his family, but he wanted to get Rikki-tikki off his guard. So he dropped his head a little, and put it on one side.

'Let us talk,' he said. 'You eat eggs. Why should not I eat birds?'

'Behind you! Look behind you!' sang Darzee.

Rikki-tikki knew better than to waste time in staring. He jumped up in the air as high as he could go, and just under him whizzed by the head of Nagaina, Nag's wicked wife. She had crept up behind him as he was talking, to make an end of him; and he heard her savage hiss as the stroke missed. He came down almost across her back, and if he had been an old mongoose he would have known that then was the time to break her back with one bite; but he was afraid of the terrible lashing return-stroke of the cobra. He bit, indeed, but did not bite long enough, and he jumped clear of the whisking tail, leaving Nagaina torn and angry.

'Wicked, wicked Darzee!' said Nag, lashing up as high as he could reach toward the nest in the thorn-bush; but

Darzee had built it out of reach of snakes, and it only swayed to and fro.

Rikki-tikki felt his eyes growing red and hot (when a mongoose's eyes grow red, he is angry), and he sat back on his tail and hind legs like a little kangaroo, and looked all round him, and chattered with rage. But Nag and Nagaina had disappeared into the grass. When a snake misses its stroke, it never says anything or gives any sign of what it means to do next. Rikki-tikki did not care to follow them, for he did not feel sure that he could manage two snakes at once. So he trotted off to the gravel path near the house, and sat down to think. It was a serious matter for him.

If you read the old books of natural history, you will find they say that when the mongoose fights the snake and happens to get bitten, he runs off and eats some herb that cures him. That is not true. The victory is only a matter of quickness of eye and quickness of foot,—snake's blow against mongoose's jump,—and as no eye can follow the motion of a snake's head when it strikes, that makes things much more wonderful than any magic herb. Rikki-tikki knew he was a young mongoose, and it made him all the more pleased to think that he had managed to escape a blow from behind. It gave him confidence in himself, and when Teddy came running down the path, Rikki-tikki was ready to be petted.

But just as Teddy was stooping, something flinched a little in the dust, and a tiny voice said: 'Be careful. I am death!' It was Karait, the dusty brown snakeling that lies for choice on the dusty earth; and his bite is as dangerous as the cobra's. But he is so small that nobody thinks of him, and so he does the more harm to people.

Rikki-tikki's eyes grew red again, and he danced up to Karait with the peculiar rocking, swaying motion that he had inherited from his family. It looks very funny, but it is so perfectly balanced a gait that you can fly off from it at any angle you please; and in dealing with snakes this is an advantage. If Rikki-tikki had only known, he was doing a much more dangerous thing than fighting Nag, for Karait is so small, and can turn so quickly, that unless Rikki bit him close to the back of the head, he would get the return-stroke in his eye or lip. But Rikki did not know: his eyes were all red, and he rocked back and forth, looking for a good place to hold. Karait struck out. Rikki jumped sideways and tried to run in, but the wicked little dusty gray head lashed within a fraction of his shoulder, and he had to jump over the body, and the head followed his heels close.

Teddy shouted to the house: 'Oh, look here! Our mongoose is killing a snake'; and Rikki-tikki heard a scream from Teddy's mother. His father ran out with a stick, but by the time he came up, Karait had lunged out once too far, and Rikki-tikki had sprung, jumped on the snake's back, dropped his head far between his fore-legs, bitten as high up the back as he could get hold, and rolled away. That bite paralysed Karait, and Rikki-tikki was just going to eat him up from the tail, after the custom of his family at dinner, when he remembered that a full meal makes a slow mongoose, and if he wanted all his strength and quickness ready, he must keep himself thin.

He went away for a dust-bath under the castor-oil bushes, while Teddy's father beat the dead Karait. 'What is the use of that?' thought Rikki-tikki. 'I have settled it all'; and then Teddy's mother picked him up from the dust and hugged him, crying that he had saved Teddy from death, and Teddy's father said that he was a providence, and Teddy looked on with big scared eyes. Rikki-tikki was rather amused at all the fuss, which, of course, he did not understand. Teddy's mother might just as well have petted Teddy for playing in the dust. Rikki was thoroughly enjoying himself.

That night, at dinner, walking to and fro among the wine-glasses on the table, he could have stuffed himself three times over with nice things; but he remembered Nag and Nagaina, and though it was very pleasant to be patted and petted by Teddy's mother, and to sit on Teddy's shoulder, his eyes would get red from time to time, and he would go off into his long war cry of '*Rikk-tikk-tikki-tikki-tchk!*'

Teddy carried him off to bed, and insisted on Rikki-tikki sleeping under his chin. Rikki-tikki was too well bred to bite or scratch, but as soon as Teddy was asleep he went off for his nightly walk round the house, and in the dark he ran up against Chuchundra, the musk-rat, creeping round by the wall. Chuchundra is a broken-hearted little beast, He whimpers and cheeps all the night, trying to make up his mind to run into the middle of the room, but he never gets there.

'Don't kill me,' said Chuchundra, almost weeping. 'Rikki-tikki, don't kill me.'

'Do you think a snake-killer kills musk-rats?' said Rikki-tikki scornfully.

'Those who kill snakes get killed by snakes,' said Chuchundra, more sorrowfully than ever. 'And how am I to be sure that Nag won't mistake me for you some dark night?'

'There's not the least danger,' said Rikki-tikki; 'but Nag is in the garden, and I know you don't go there.'

'My cousin Chua, the rat, told me——' said Chuchundra, and then he stopped.

'Told you what?'

'H'sh! Nag is everywhere, Rikki-tikki. You should have talked to Chua in the garden.'

'I didn't—so you must tell me. Quick, Chuchundra, or I'll bite you!'

Chuchundra sat down and cried till the tears rolled off his whiskers. 'I am a very poor man,' he sobbed. 'I never had spirit enough to run out into the middle of the room. H'sh! I mustn't tell you anything. Can't you *hear*, Rikki-tikki?'

Rikki-tikki listened. The house was as still as still, but he thought he could just catch the faintest *scratch-scratch* in the world,—a noise as faint as that of a wasp walking on a window-pane,—the dry scratch of a snake's scales on brick-work.

'That's Nag or Nagaina,' he said to himself; 'and he's crawling into the bath-room sluice. You're right, Chuchundra; I should have talked to Chua.'

He stole off to Teddy's bath-room, but there was nothing there, and then to Teddy's mother's bath-room. At the bottom of the smooth plaster wall there was a brick pulled out to make a sluice for the bath-water, and as Rikki-tikki stole in by the masonry curb where the bath is put, he heard Nag and Nagaina whispering together outside in the moonlight.

'When the house is emptied of people,' said Nagaina to her husband, '*he* will have to go away, and then the garden will be our own again. Go in quietly, and remember that the big man who killed Karait is the first one to bite. Then come out and tell me, and we will hunt for Rikki-tikki together.'

'But are you sure that there is anything to be gained by killing the people?' said Nag.

'Everything. When there were no people in the bungalow, did we have any mongoose in the garden? So long as the bungalow is empty, we are king and queen of the garden; and remember that as soon as our eggs in the melon-bed hatch (as they may to-morrow), our children will need room and quiet.'

I had not thought of that,' said Nag. 'I will go, but there is no need that we should hunt for Rikki-tikki afterward. I will kill the big man and his wife, and the child if

I can, and come away quietly. Then the bungalow will be empty, and Rikki-tikki will go.'

Rikki-tikki tingled all over with rage and hatred at this, and then Nag's head came through the sluice, and his five feet of cold body followed it. Angry as he was, Rikki-tikki was very frightened as he saw the size of the big cobra. Nag coiled himself up, raised his head, and looked into the bath-room in the dark, and Rikki could see his eyes glitter.

'Now, if I kill him here, Nagaina will know; and if I fight him on the open floor, the odds are in his favour. What am I to do?' said Rikki-tikki-tavi.

Nag waved to and fro, and then Rikki-tikki heard him drinking from the biggest water-jar that was used to fill the bath. 'That is good,' said the snake. 'Now, when Karait was killed, the big man had a stick. He may have that stick still, but when he comes in to bathe in the morning he will not have a stick. I shall wait here till he comes. Nagaina—do you hear me?—I shall wait here in the cool till daytime.'

There was no answer from outside, so Rikki-tikki knew Nagaina had gone away. Nag coiled himself down, coil by coil, round the bulge at the bottom of the water-jar, and Rikki-tikki stayed still as death. After an hour he began to move, muscle by muscle, toward the jar. Nag was asleep, and Rikki-tikki looked at his big back, wondering which would be the best place for a good hold. 'If I don't break his back at the first jump,' said Rikki, 'he can still fight; and if he fights—O Rikki!' He looked at the thickness of the neck below the hood, but that was too much for him; and a bite near the tail would only make Nag savage.

'It must be the head,' he said at last; 'the head above the hood; and when I am once there, I must not let go.'

Then he jumped. The head was lying a little clear of the water-jar, under the curve of it; and, as his teeth met,

Rikki braced his back against the bulge of the red earthenware to hold down the head. This gave him just one second's purchase, and he made the most of it. Then he was battered to and fro as a rat is shaken by a dog—to and fro on the floor, up and down, and round in great circles; but his eyes were red, and he held on as the body cart-whipped over the floor, upsetting the tin dipper and the soap-dish and the flesh-brush, and banged against the tin side of the bath. As he held he closed his jaws tighter and tighter, for he made sure he would be banged to death, and, for the honour of his family, he preferred to be found with his teeth locked. He was dizzy, aching, and felt shaken to pieces when something went off like a thunderclap just behind him; a hot wind knocked him senseless, and red fire singed his fur. The big man had been wakened by the noise, and had fired both barrels of a shot-gun into Nag just behind the hood.

Rikki-tikki held on with his eyes shut, for now he was quite sure he was dead; but the head did not move, and the big man picked him up and said: 'It's the mongoose again, Alice; the little chap has saved *our* lives now.' Then Teddy's mother came in with a very white face, and saw what was left of Nag, and Rikki-tikki dragged himself to Teddy's bedroom and spent half the rest of the night shaking himself tenderly to find out whether he really was broken into forty pieces, as he fancied.

When morning came he was very stiff, but well pleased with his doings. 'Now I have Nagaina to settle with, and she will be worse than five Nags, and there's no knowing when the eggs she spoke of will hatch. Goodness! I must go and see Darzee,' he said.

Without waiting for breakfast, Rikki-tikki ran to the thorn-bush where Darzee was singing a song of triumph at the top of his voice. The news of Nag's death was all over the garden, for the sweeper had thrown the body on the rubbish-heap.

'Oh, you stupid tuft of feathers!' said Rikki-tikki angrily. 'Is this the time to sing?'

'Nag is dead—is dead—is dead!' sang Darzee. 'The valiant Rikki-tikki caught him by the head and held fast. The big man brought the bang-stick, and Nag fell in two pieces! He will never eat my babies again.'

'All that's true enough; but where's Nagaina?' said Rikki-tikki, looking carefully round him.

'Nagaina came to the bath-room sluice and called for Nag,' Darzee went on; 'and Nag came out on the end of a stick—the sweeper picked him up on the end of a stick and threw him upon the rubbish-heap. Let us sing about the great, the red-eyed Rikki-tikki!' and Darzee filled his throat and sang.

'If I could get up to your nest, I'd roll all your babies out!' said Rikki-tikki. 'You don't know when to do the right thing at the right time. You're safe enough in your nest there, but it's war for me down here. Stop singing a minute, Darzee.'

'For the great, the beautiful Rikki-tikki's sake I will stop,' said Darzee. 'What is it, O killer of the terrible Nag?'

'Where is Nagaina, for the third time?'

'On the rubbish-heap by the stables, mourning for Nag. Great is Rikki-tikki with the white teeth.'

'Bother my white teeth! Have you ever heard where she keeps her eggs?'

'In the melon-bed, on the end nearest the wall, where the sun strikes nearly all day. She hid them three weeks ago.'

'And you never thought it worth while to tell me? The end nearest the wall, you said?'

'Rikki-tikki, you are not going to eat her eggs?"

'Not eat exactly; no. Darzee, if you have a grain of sense you will fly off to the stables and pretend that your wing is broken, and let Nagaina chase you away to this bush! I must get to the melon-bed, and if I went there now she'd see me.'

Darzee was a feather-brained little fellow who could never hold more than one idea at a time in his head; and just because he knew that Nagaina's children were born in eggs like his own, he didn't think at first that it was fair to kill them. But his wife was a sensible bird, and she knew that cobra's eggs meant young cobras later on; so she flew off from the nest, and left Darzee to keep the babies warm, and continue his song about the death of Nag. Darzee was very like a man in some ways.

She fluttered in front of Nagaina by the rubbish-heap, and cried out, 'Oh, my wing is broken! The boy in the house threw a stone at me and broke it.' Then she fluttered more desperately than ever.

Nagaina lifted up her head and hissed, 'You warned Rikki-tikki when I would have killed him. Indeed and truly, you've chosen a bad place to be lame in.' And she moved toward Darzee's wife, slipping along over the dust.

'The boy broke it with a stone!' shrieked Darzee's wife.

'Well! It may be some consolation to you when you're dead to know that I shall settle accounts with the boy. My husband lies on the rubbish-heap this morning, but before night the boy in the house will lie very still. What is the use of running away? I am sure to catch you. Little fool, look at me!'

Darzee's wife knew better than to do *that*, for a bird who looks at a snake's eyes gets so frightened that she cannot move. Darzee's wife fluttered on, piping sorrowfully, and never leaving the ground, and Nagaina quickened her pace.

Rikki-tikki heard them going up the path from the stables, and he raced for the end of the melon-patch near the wall. There, in the warm litter about the melons, very cunningly hidden, he found twenty-five eggs, about the size of a bantam's eggs, but with whitish skin instead of shell.

'I was not a day too soon,' he said; for he could see the baby cobras curled up inside the skin, and he knew that the minute they were hatched they could each kill a man or a mongoose. He bit off the tops of the eggs as fast as he could, taking care to crush the young cobras, and turned over the litter from time to time to see whether he had missed any. At last there were only three eggs left, and Rikki-tikki began to chuckle to himself, when he heard Darzee's wife screaming:

'Rikki-tikki, I led Nagaina toward the house, and she has gone into the verandah, and—oh, come quickly—she means killing!'

Rikki-tikki smashed two eggs, and tumbled backward down the melon-bed with the third egg in his mouth, and scuttled to the verandah as hard as he could put foot to the ground. Teddy and his mother and father were there at early breakfast; but Rikki-tikki saw that they were not eating anything. They sat stone-still, and their faces were white. Nagaina was coiled up on the matting by Teddy's chair, within easy striking distance of Teddy's bare leg, and she was swaying to and fro singing a song of triumph.

'Son of the big man that killed Nag,' she hissed, 'stay still. I am not ready yet. Wait a little. Keep very still, all you three. If you move I strike, and if you do not move I strike. Oh, foolish people, who killed my Nag!'

Teddy's eyes were fixed on his father, and all his father could do was to whisper, 'Sit still, Teddy. You mustn't move. Teddy, keep still.'

Then Rikki-tikki came up and cried: 'Turn round, Nagaina; turn and fight!'

'All in good time,' said she, without moving her eyes. 'I will settle my account with *you* presently. Look at your friends, Rikki-tikki. They are still and white; they are afraid. They dare not move, and if you come a step nearer I strike.'

'Look at your eggs,' said Rikki-tikki, 'in the melon-bed near the wall. Go and look, Nagaina.'

The big snake turned half round, and saw the egg on the verandah. 'Ah-h! Give it to me,' she said.

Rikki-tikki put his paws one on each side of the egg, and his eyes were blood-red. 'What price for a snake's egg? For a young cobra? For a young king-cobra? For the last—the very last of the brood? The ants are eating all the others down by the melon-bed.'

Nagaina spun clear round, forgetting everything for the sake of the one egg; and Rikki-tikki saw Teddy's father shoot out a big hand, catch Teddy by the shoulder, and drag him across the little table with the tea-cups, safe and out of reach of Nagaina.

'Tricked! Tricked! Tricked! *Rikk-tck-tck!*' chuckled Rikki-tikki. 'The boy is safe, and it was I—I—I that caught Nag by the hood last night in the bath-room.' Then he began to jump up and down, all four feet together, his head close to the floor. 'He threw me to and fro, but he could not shake me off. He was dead before the big man blew him in two. I did it. *Rikki-tikki-tck-tck!* Come then, Nagaina. Come and fight with me. You shall not be a widow long.'

Nagaina saw that she had lost her chance of killing Teddy, and the egg lay between Rikki-tikki's paws. 'Give me the egg, Rikki-tikki. Give me the last of my eggs, and I will go away and never come back,' she said, lowering her hood

'Yes, you will go away, and you will never come back; for you will go to the rubbish-heap with Nag. Fight, widow! The big man has gone for his gun! Fight!'

Rikki-tikki was bounding all round Nagaina keeping just

out of reach of her stroke, his little eyes like hot coals. Nagaina gathered herself together, and flung out at him. Rikki-tikki jumped up and backward. Again and again and again she struck, and each time her head came with a whack on the matting of the verandah, and she gathered herself together like a watch-spring. Then Rikki tikki danced in a circle to get behind her, and Nagaina spun round to keep her head to his head, so that the rustle of her tail on the matting sounded like dry leaves blown along by the wind.

He had forgotten the egg. It still lay on the verandah, and Nagaina came nearer and nearer to it, till at last, while Rikki-tikki was drawing breath, she caught it in her mouth, turned to the verandah steps and flew like an arrow down the path, with Rikki-tikki behind her. When the cobra runs for her life, she goes like a whip-lash flicked across a horse's neck.

Rikki-tikki knew that he must catch her, or all the trouble would begin again. She headed straight for the long grass by the thorn-bush, and as he was running Rikki-tikki heard Darzee still singing his foolish little song of triumph. But Darzee's wife was wiser She flew off her nest as Nagaina came along and flapped her wings about Nagaina's head. If Darzee had helped they might have turned her; but Nagaina only lowered her hood and went on. Still, the instant's delay brought Rikki-tikki up to her, and as she plunged into the rat-hole where she and Nag used to live, his little white teeth were clenched on her tail, and he went down with her—and very few mongooses, however wise and old they may be, care to follow a cobra into its hole. It was dark in the hole; and Rikki-tikki never knew when it might open out and give Nagaina room to turn and strike at him. He held on savagely, and struck out his feet to act as brakes on the dark slope of the hot, moist earth.

Then the grass by the mouth of the hole stopped waving, and Darzee said: 'It is all over with Rikki-tikki! We must sing his death-song. Valiant Rikki-tikki is dead! For Nagaina will surely kill him underground.'

So he sang a very mournful song that he made up on the spur of the minute, and just as he got to the most touching part the grass quivered again, and Rikki-tikki, covered with dirt, dragged himself out of the hole leg by leg, licking his whiskers. Darzee stopped with a little shout. Rikki-tikki shook some of the dust out of his fur and sneezed. 'It is all over,' he said. 'The widow will never come out again.' And the red ants that live between the grass stems heard him, and began to troop down one after another to see if he had spoken the truth.

Rikki-tikki curled himself up in the grass and slept where he was—slept and slept till it was late in the afternoon, for he had done a hard day's work.

'Now,' he said, when he awoke, 'I will go back to the house. Tell the Coppersmith, Darzee, and he will tell the garden that Nagaina is dead.'

The Coppersmith is a bird who makes a noise exactly like the beating of a little hammer on a copper pot; and the reason he is always making it is because he is the town-crier to every Indian garden, and tells all the news to everybody who cares to listen. As Rikki-tikki went up the path, he heard his 'attention' notes like a tiny dinner-gong; and then the steady '*Ding-dong-tock!* Nag is dead—*dong!* Nagaina is dead! *Ding-dong-tock!*' That set all the birds in the garden singing, and the frogs croaking; for Nag and Nagaina used to eat frogs as well as little birds.

When Rikki got to the house, Teddy and Teddy's mother (she looked very white still, for she had been fainting) and Teddy's father came out and almost cried over him; and that night he ate all that was given him till he could eat no more, and went to bed on Teddy's shoulder, where

Teddy's mother saw him when she came to look late at night.

'He saved our lives and Teddy's life,' she said to her husband. 'Just think, he saved all our lives.'

Rikki-tikki woke up with a jump, for all the mongooses are light sleepers.

'Oh, it's you,' said he. 'What are you bothering for? All the cobras are dead; and if they weren't, I'm here.'

Rikki-tikki had a right to be proud of himself; but he did not grow too proud, and he kept that garden as a mongoose should keep it, with tooth and jump and spring and bite, till never a cobra dared show its head inside the walls.

DARZEE'S CHAUNT.

(SUNG IN HONOUR OF RIKKI-TIKKI-TAVI.)

SINGER and tailor am I—
Doubled the joys that I know—
Proud of my lilt through the sky,
Proud of the house that I sew—
Over and under, so weave I my music—so weave I the house that I sew.

Sing to your fledglings again,
Mother, oh lift up your head!
Evil that plagued us is slain,
Death in the garden lies dead.
Terror that hid in the roses is impotent—flung on the dung-hill and dead!

Who hath delivered us, who?
Tell me his nest and his name.
Rikki, the valiant, the true,
Tikki, with eyeballs of flame,
Rik-tikki-tikki, the ivory-fanged, the hunter with eyeballs of flame.

Give him the Thanks of the Birds,
Bowing with tail-feathers spread!
Praise him with nightingale words—
Nay, I will praise him instead.
Hear! I will sing you the praise of the bottle-tailed Rikki, with eyeballs of red!

(*Here Rikki-tikki interrupted, and the rest of the song is lost.*)

WILLIAM THE CONQUEROR

PART I

> I have done one braver thing
> Than all the worthies did;
> And yet a braver thence doth spring,
> Which is to keep that hid.
>
> THE UNDERTAKING.

'Is it officially declared yet?'

'They've gone as far as to admit extreme local scarcity, and they've started relief-works in one or two districts, the paper says.'

'That means it will be declared as soon as they can make sure of the men and the rolling-stock. Shouldn't wonder if it were as bad as the Big Famine.'

'Can't be,' said Scott, turning a little in the long cane chair. 'We've had fifteen-anna crops in the north, and Bombay and Bengal report more than they know what to do with. They'll be able to check it before it gets out of hand. It will only be local.'

Martyn picked up the *Pioneer* from the table, read through the telegrams once more, and put up his feet on the chair-rests. It was a hot, dark, breathless evening, heavy with the smell of the newly-watered Mall. The flowers in the Club gardens were dead and black on their stalks, the little lotus-pond was a circle of caked mud, and the tamarisk-trees were white with the dust of days. Most of the men were at the bandstand in the public gardens—from the Club verandah you could hear the native Police band hammering stale waltzes—or on the polo-ground or in the high-walled fives-court, hotter than a Dutch oven. Half a dozen grooms, squatted at the heads of their ponies, waited their masters' return. From time to time a man would ride at a foot-pace into the Club compound, and listlessly loaf over to the whitewashed barracks beside the main building. These were supposed to be chambers. Men lived in them, meeting the same faces night after night at dinner, and drawing out their office-work till the latest possible hour, that they might escape that doleful company.

'What are you going to do?' said Martyn, with a yawn. 'Let's have a swim before dinner.'

'Water's hot,' said Scott. 'I was at the bath to-day.'

'Play you game o' billiards—fifty up.'

'It's a hundred and five in the hall now. Sit still and don't be so abominably energetic.'

A grunting camel swung up to the porch, his badged and belted rider fumbling a leather pouch.

'*Kubber-kargaz—ki—yektraaa*,' the man whined, handing down the newspaper extra—a slip printed on one side only, and damp from the press. It was pinned on the green baize-board, between notices of ponies for sale and fox-terriers missing.

Martyn rose lazily, read it, and whistled. 'It's declared!' he cried. 'One, two, three—eight districts go under the operation of the Famine Code *ek dum*. They've put Jimmy Hawkins in charge.'

'Good business!' said Scott, with the first sign of interest he had shown. 'When in doubt hire a Punjabi. I worked under Jimmy when I first came out and he belonged to the Punjab. He has more *bundobust* than most men.'

'Jimmy's a Jubilee Knight now,' said Martyn. 'He was a good chap, even though he is a thrice-born civilian and went to the Benighted Presidency. What unholy names these Madras districts rejoice in—all *ungas* or *rungas* or *pillays* or *polliums*.'

A dog-cart drove up, and a man entered, mopping his head. He was editor of the one daily paper at the capital of a province of twenty-five million natives and a few hundred white men, and as his staff was limited to himself and one assistant, his office hours ran variously from ten to twenty a day.

'Hi, Raines; you're supposed to know everything,' said Martyn, stopping him. 'How's this Madras "scarcity" going to turn out?'

'No one knows as yet. There's a message as long as your arm coming in on the telephone. I've left my cub to fill it out. Madras has owned she can't manage it alone, and Jimmy seems to have a free hand in getting all the men he needs. Arbuthnot's warned to hold himself in readiness.'

'"Badger" Arbuthnot?'

'The Peshawur chap. Yes, and the *Pi* wires that Ellis and Clay have been moved from the North-West already, and they've taken half a dozen Bombay men, too. It's *pukka* famine, by the looks of it.'

'They're nearer the scene of action than we are; but if it comes to indenting on the Punjab this early, there's more in this than meets the eye,' said Martyn.

'Here to-day and gone to-morrow. Didn't come to stay for ever,' said Scott, dropping one of Marryat's novels, and rising to his feet. 'Martyn, your sister's waiting for you.'

A rough gray horse was backing and shifting at the edge of the verandah, where the light of a kerosene-lamp fell on a brown calico habit and a white face under a gray felt hat.

'Right, O,' said Martyn. 'I'm ready. Better come and

dine with us if you've nothing to do, Scott. William, is there any dinner in the house?'

'I'll go home first and see,' was the rider's answer. 'You can drive him over—at eight, remember.'

Scott moved leisurely to his room, and changed into the evening-dress of the season and the country: spotless white linen from head to foot, with a broad silk *cummerbund*. Dinner at the Martyns' was a decided improvement on the goat-mutton, twiney-tough fowl, and tinned entrées of the Club. But it was a great pity Martyn could not afford to send his sister to the Hills for the hot weather. As an Acting District Superintendent of Police, Martyn drew the magnificent pay of six hundred depreciated silver rupees a month, and his little four-roomed bungalow said just as much. There were the usual blue-and-white striped jail-made rugs on the uneven floor; the usual glass-studded Amritsar *phulkaris* draped to nails driven into the flaking whitewash of the walls; the usual half-dozen chairs that did not match, picked up at sales of dead men's effects; and the usual streaks of black grease where the leather punka-thong ran through the wall. It was as though everything had been unpacked the night before to be repacked next morning. Not a door in the house was true on its hinges. The little windows, fifteen feet up, were darkened with wasp-nests, and lizards hunted flies between the beams of the wood-ceiled roof. But all this was part of Scott's life. Thus did people live who had such an income; and in a land where each man's pay, age, and position are printed in a book, that all may read, it is hardly worth while to play at pretences in word or deed. Scott counted eight years' service in the Irrigation Department, and drew eight hundred rupees a month, on the understanding that if he served the State faithfully for another twenty-two years he could retire on a pension of some four hundred rupees a month. His working life, which had been spent chiefly under canvas or in temporary shelters where a man could sleep, eat, and write letters, was bound up with the opening and guarding of irrigation canals, the handling of two or three thousand workmen of all castes and creeds, and the payment of vast sums of coined silver. He had finished that spring, not without credit, the last section of the great Mosuhl Canal, and—much against his will, for he hated office work—had been sent in to serve during the hot weather on the accounts and supply side of the Department, with sole charge of the sweltering sub-office at the capital of the Province. Martyn knew this; William, his sister, knew it; and everybody knew it.

Scott knew, too, as well as the rest of the world, that Miss Martyn had come out to India four years before, to keep house for her brother, who, as everyone, again, knew, had borrowed the money to pay for her passage, and that she ought, as all the world said, to have married long ago. Instead of this, she had refused some half a dozen subalterns, a civilian twenty years her senior, one major, and a man in the Indian Medical Department. This, too, was common property. She had 'stayed down three hot weathers,' as the saying is, because her brother was in debt and could not afford the expense of her keep at even a cheap hill-station. Therefore her face was white as bone, and in the centre of her forehead was a big silvery scar about the size of a shilling—the mark of a Delhi sore, which is the same as a 'Bagdad date.' This comes from drinking bad water, and slowly eats into the flesh till it is ripe enough to be burned out with acids.

None the less William had enjoyed herself hugely in her four years. Twice she had been nearly drowned while fording a river on horseback; once she had been run away with on a camel; had witnessed a midnight attack of thieves on her brother's camp; had seen justice administered with long sticks, in the open under trees; could speak Urdu and even rough Punjabi with a fluency that was envied by her seniors; had altogether fallen out of the habit of writing to her aunts in England, or cutting the pages of the English magazines; had been through a very bad cholera year, seeing sights unfit to be told; and had wound up her experiences by six weeks of typhoid fever, during which her head had been shaved; and hoped to keep her twenty-third birthday that September. It is conceivable that her aunts would not have approved of a girl who never set foot on the ground if a horse were within hail; who rode to dances with a shawl thrown over her skirt; who wore her hair cropped and curling all over her head; who answered indifferently to the name of William or Bill; whose speech was heavy with the flowers of the vernacular; who could act in amateur theatricals, play on the banjo, rule eight servants and two horses, their accounts and their diseases, and look men slowly and deliberately between the eyes—yea, after they had proposed to her and been rejected.

'I like men who do things,' she had confided to a man in the Educational Department, who was teaching the sons of cloth merchants and dyers the beauty of Wordsworth's 'Excursion' in annotated cram-books; and when he grew poetical, William explained that she 'didn't understand poetry very much; it made her head ache,' and another broken heart took refuge at the Club. But it was all William's fault. She delighted in hearing men talk of their own work, and that is the most fatal way of bringing a man to your feet.

Scott had known her more or less for some three years, meeting her, as a rule, under canvas when his camp and her brother's joined for a day on the edge of the Indian Desert. He had danced with her several times at the big Christmas gatherings, when as many as five hundred white people came into the station; and he had always a great respect for her housekeeping and her dinners.

She looked more like a boy than ever when, after their meal, she sat, one foot tucked under her, on the leather camp-sofa, rolling cigarettes for her brother, her low forehead puckered beneath the dark curls as she twiddled the papers. She stuck out her rounded chin when the tobacco stayed in place, and, with a gesture as true as a school-boy's throwing a stone, tossed the finished article across the room to Martyn, who caught it with one hand, and continued his talk with Scott. It was all 'shop,'—canals and the policing of canals; the sins of villagers who stole more water than they had paid for, and the grosser sin of native constables who connived at the thefts; of the transplanting bodily of villages to newly-irrigated ground, and of the coming fight with the desert in the south when the Provincial funds should warrant the opening of the long-surveyed Luni Protective Canal System. And Scott spoke openly of his great desire to be put on one particular section of the work where he knew the land and the people, and Martyn sighed for a billet in the Himalayan foot-hills, and spoke his mind of his superiors, and William rolled cigarettes and said nothing, but smiled gravely on her brother because he was happy.

At ten Scott's horse came to the door, and the evening was ended.

The lights of the two low bungalows in which the daily paper was printed showed bright across the road. It was too early to try to find sleep, and Scott drifted over to the editor. Raines, stripped to the waist like a sailor at a gun, lay in a long chair, waiting for night telegrams. He had a theory that if a man did not stay by his work all day and most of the night he laid himself open to fever; so he ate and slept among his files.

'Can you do it?' he said drowsily. 'I didn't mean to bring you over.'

'About what? I've been dining at the Martyns'.'

'The famine, of course, Martyn's warned for it, too. They're taking men where they can find 'em. I sent a note to you at the Club just now, asking if you could do us a letter once a week from the south—between two and three columns, say. Nothing sensational, of course, but just plain facts about who is doing what, and so forth. Our regular rates—ten rupees a column.'

'Sorry, but it's out of my line,' Scott answered, staring absently at the map of India on the wall. 'It's rough on Martyn—very. Wonder what he'll do with his sister. Wonder what the deuce they'll do with me? I've no famine experience. This is the first I've heard of it. *Am* I ordered?'

'Oh, yes. Here's the wire. They'll put you on relief-works,' Raines went on, 'with a horde of Madrassis dying like flies; one native apothecary and half a pint of cholera-mixture among the ten thousand of you. It comes of your being idle for the moment. Every man who isn't doing two men's work seems to have been called upon. Hawkins evidently believes in Punjabis. It's going to be quite as bad as anything they have had in the last ten years.'

'It's all in the day's work, worse luck. I suppose I shall get my orders officially some time to-morrow. I'm glad I happened to drop in. Better go and pack my kit now. Who relieves me here—do you know?'

Raines turned over a sheaf of telegrams. 'McEuan,' said he, 'from Murree.'

Scott chuckled. 'He thought he was going to be cool all summer. He'll be very sick about this. Well, no good talking. Night.'

Two hours later, Scott, with a clear conscience, laid himself down to rest on a string cot in a bare room. Two worn bullock-trunks, a leather water-bottle, a tin ice-box, and his pet saddle sewed up in sacking were piled at the door, and the Club secretary's receipt for last month's bill was under his pillow. His orders came next morning, and with them an unofficial telegram from Sir James Hawkins, who did not forget good men, bidding him report himself with all speed at some unpronounceable place fifteen hundred miles to the south, for the famine was sore in the land, and white men were needed.

A pink and fattish youth arrived in the red-hot noonday, whimpering a little at fate and famines, which never allowed any one three months' peace. He was Scott's successor—another cog in the machinery, moved forward behind his fellow, whose services, as the official announcement ran, 'were placed at the disposal of the Madras Government for famine duty until further orders.' Scott handed over the funds in his charge, showed him the coolest corner in the office, warned him against excess of zeal, and, as twilight fell, departed from the Club in a hired carriage, with his faithful body servant, Faiz Ullah, and a mound of disordered baggage atop, to catch the Southern Mail at the loopholed and bastioned railway-station. The heat from the thick brick walls struck him across the face as if it had been a hot towel, and he reflected that there were at least five nights and four days of travel before him. Faiz Ullah, used to the chances of service, plunged into the crowd on the stone platform, while Scott, a black cheroot between his teeth, waited till his compartment should be set away. A dozen native policemen, with their rifles and bundles, shouldered into the press of Punjabi farmers, Sikh craftsmen, and greasy-locked Afreedee pedlars, escorting with all pomp Martyn's uniform case, water-bottles, ice-box, and bedding-roll. They saw Faiz Ullah's lifted hand, and steered for it.

'My Sahib and your Sahib,' said Faiz Ullah to Martyn's man, 'will travel together. Thou and I, O brother, will thus secure the servants' places close by, and because of our masters' authority none will dare to disturb us.'

When Faiz Ullah reported all things ready, Scott settled down coatless and bootless on the broad leather-covered bunk. The heat under the iron-arched roof of the station might have been anything over a hundred degrees. At the last moment Martyn entered, hot and dripping.

'Don't swear,' said Scott, lazily; 'it's too late to change your carriage; and we'll divide the ice.'

'What are you doing here?' said the policeman.

'Lent to the Madras Government, same as you. By Jove, it's a bender of a night! Are you taking any of your men down?'

'A dozen. Suppose I'll have to superintend relief distributions. Didn't know you were under orders too.'

'I didn't till after I left you last night. Raines had the news first. My orders came this morning. McEuan relieved me at four, and I got off at once. Shouldn't wonder if it wouldn't be a good thing—this famine—if we come through it alive.'

'Jimmy ought to put you and me to work together,' said Martyn; and then, after a pause: 'My sister's here.'

'Good business,' said Scott, heartily. 'Going to get off at Umballa, I suppose, and go up to Simla. Who'll she stay with there?'

'No-o; that's just the trouble of it. She's going down with me.'

Scott sat bolt upright under the oil lamp as the train jolted past Tarn-Taran station. 'What! You don't mean you couldn't afford—'

'Oh, I'd have scraped up the money somehow.'

'You might have come to me, to begin with,' said Scott, stiffly; 'we aren't altogether strangers.'

'Well, you needn't be stuffy about it. I might, but—you don't know my sister. I've been explaining and exhorting and entreating and commanding and all the rest of it all day--lost my temper since seven this morning, and haven't got it back yet—but she wouldn't hear of any compromise. A woman's entitled to travel with her husband if she wants to, and William says she's on the same footing. You see, we've been together all our lives, more or less, since my people died. It isn't as if she were an ordinary sister.'

'All the sisters I've ever heard of would have stayed where they were well off.'

'She's as clever as a man, confound her,' Martyn went on. 'She broke up the bungalow over my head while I was talking at her. Settled the whole *subchiz* [outfit] in three hours—servants, horses, and all. I didn't get my orders till nine.'

'Jimmy Hawkins won't be pleased,' said Scott. 'A famine's no place for a woman.'

'Mrs. Jim—I mean Lady Jim's in camp with him. At any rate, she says she will look after my sister. William wired down to her on her own responsibility, asking if she could come, and knocked the ground from under me by showing me her answer.'

Scott laughed aloud. 'If she can do that she can take care of herself, and Mrs. Jim won't let her run into any mischief. There aren't many women, sisters or wives, who would walk into a famine with their eyes open. It isn't as if she didn't know what these things mean. She was through the Jaloo cholera last year.'

The train stopped at Amritsar, and Scott went back to the ladies' compartment, immediately behind their carriage. William, a cloth riding-cap on her curls, nodded affably.

'Come in and have some tea,' she said. 'Best thing in the world for heat-apoplexy.'

'Do I look as if I were going to have heat-apoplexy?'

'Never can tell,' said William, wisely. 'It's always best to be ready.'

She had arranged her belongings with the knowledge of

an old campaigner. A felt-covered water-bottle hung in the draught of one of the shuttered windows; a tea-set of Russian china, packed in a wadded basket, stood ready on the seat; and a travelling spirit-lamp was clamped against the woodwork above it.

William served them generously, in large cups, hot tea, which saves the veins of the neck from swelling inopportunely on a hot night. It was characteristic of the girl that, her plan of action once settled, she asked for no comments on it. Life with men who had a great deal of work to do, and very little time to do it in, had taught her the wisdom of effacing as well as of fending for herself. She did not by word or deed suggest that she would be useful, comforting, or beautiful in their travels, but continued about her business serenely: put the cups back without clatter when tea was ended, and made cigarettes for her guests.

'This time last night,' said Scott, 'we didn't expect—er—this kind of thing, did we?'

'I've learned to expect anything,' said William. 'You know, in our service, we live at the end of the telegraph; but, of course, this ought to be a good thing for us all, departmentally—if we live.'

'It knocks us out of the running in our own Province,' Scott replied, with equal gravity. 'I hoped to be put on the Luni Protective Works this cold weather; but there's no saying how long the famine may keep us.'

'Hardly beyond October, I should think,' said Martyn. 'It will be ended, one way or the other, then.'

'And we've nearly a week of this,' said William. 'Sha'n't we be dusty when it's over?'

For a night and a day they knew their surroundings; and for a night and a day, skirting the edge of the great Indian Desert on a narrow-gauge line, they remembered how in the days of their apprenticeship they had come by that road from Bombay. Then the languages in which the names of the stations were written changed, and they launched south into a foreign land, where the very smells were new. Many long and heavily-laden grain trains were in front of them, and they could feel the hand of Jimmy Hawkins from far off. They waited in extemporised sidings blocked by processions of empty trucks returning to the north, and were coupled on to slow, crawling trains, and dropped at midnight, Heaven knew where; but it was furiously hot; and they walked to and fro among sacks, and dogs howled.

Then they came to an India more strange to them than to the untravelled Englishman—the flat, red India of palm-tree, palmyra-palm, and rice, the India of the picture-books, of *Little Henry and His Bearer*—all dead and dry in the baking heat. They had left the incessant passenger-traffic of the north and west far and far behind them. Here the people crawled to the side of the train, holding their little ones in their arms; and a loaded truck would be left behind, men and women clustering round and above it like ants by spilled honey. Once in the twilight they saw on a dusty plain a regiment of little brown men, each bearing a body over his shoulder; and when the train stopped to leave yet another truck, they perceived that the burdens were not corpses, but only foodless folk picked up beside their dead oxen by a corps of Irregular troops. Now they met more white men, here one and there two, whose tents stood close to the line, and who came armed with written authorities and angry words to cut off a truck. They were too busy to do more than nod at Scott and Martyn, and stare curiously at William, who could do nothing except make tea, and watch how her men staved off the rush of wailing, walking skeletons, putting them down three at a time in heaps, with their own hands uncoupling the marked trucks, or taking receipts from the hollowed-eyed, weary white men, who spoke another argot than theirs.

They ran out of ice, out of soda-water, and out of tea; for they were six days and seven nights on the road, and it seemed to them like seven times seven years.

At last, in a dry, hot dawn, in a land of death, lit by long red fires of railway sleepers, where they were burning the dead, they came to their destination, and were met by Jim Hawkins, the Head of the Famine, unshaven, unwashed, but cheery, and entirely in command of affairs.

Martyn, he decreed, then and there, was to live on trains till further orders; was to go back with empty trucks, filling them with starving people as he found them, and dropping them at a famine-camp on the edge of the Eight Districts. He would pick up supplies and return, and his constables would guard the loaded grain-cars, also picking up people, and would drop them at a camp a hundred miles south. Scott—Hawkins was very glad to see Scott again—would, that same hour, take charge of a convoy of bullock-carts, and would go south, feeding as he went, to yet another famine-camp, far from the rail, where he would leave his starving—there would be no lack of starving on the route—and wait for orders by telegraph. Generally, Scott was in all small things to do what he thought best.

William bit her under lip. There was no one in the wide world like her one brother, but Martyn's orders gave him no discretion. She came out, masked with dust from head to foot, a horse-shoe wrinkle on her forehead, put here by much thinking during the past week, but as self-possessed as ever. Mrs. Jim—who should have been Lady Jim, but that no one remembered to call her aright—took possession of her with a little gasp.

'Oh, I'm so glad you're here,' she almost sobbed. 'You oughtn't to, of course, but there—there isn't another woman in the place, and we must help each other, you know; and we've all the wretched people and the little babies they are selling.'

'I've seen some,' said William.

'Isn't it ghastly? I've bought twenty; they're in our camp; but won't you have something to eat first? We've more than ten people can do here; and I've got a horse for you. Oh, I'm so glad you've come! You're a Punjabi too, you know.'

'Steady, Lizzie,' said Hawkins, over his shoulder. 'We'll look after you, Miss Martyn. Sorry I can't ask you to breakfast, Martyn. You'll have to eat as you go. Leave two of your men to help Scott. These poor devils can't stand up to load carts. Saunders' (this to the engine-driver, half asleep in the cab), 'back down and get those empties away.' You've 'line clear' to Anundrapillay; they'll give you orders north of that. Scott, load up your carts from that B. P. P. truck, and be off as soon as you can. The Eurasian in the pink shirt is your interpreter and guide. You'll find an apothecary of sorts tied to the yoke of the second wagon. He's been trying to bolt; you'll have to look after him. Lizzie, drive Miss Martyn to camp, and tell them to send the red horse down here for me.'

Scott, with Faiz Ullah and two policemen, was already busy on the carts, backing them up to the truck and unbolting the sideboards quietly, while the others pitched in the bags of millet and wheat. Hawkins watched him for as long as it took to fill one cart.

'That's a good man,' he said. 'If all goes well I shall work him—hard.' This was Jim Hawkins's notion of the highest compliment one human being could pay another.

An hour later Scott was under way; the apothecary threatening him with the penalties of the law for that he, a member of the Subordinate Medical Department, had been coerced and bound against his will and all laws governing the liberty of the subject; the pink-shirted Eurasian begging leave to see his mother, who happened to be dying some three miles away: 'Only verree, verree short leave of absence, and will presently return, sar—'; the two constables, armed with staves, bringing up the rear; and Faiz Ullah, a Mohammedan's contempt for all Hindoos and foreigners in every line of his face, explaining to the drivers that though Scott Sahib was a man to be feared on all fours, he, Faiz Ullah, was Authority itself.

The procession creaked past Hawkins's camp—three stained tents under a clump of dead trees; behind them the famine-shed where a crowd of hopeless ones tossed their arms around the cooking-kettles.

'Wish to Heaven William had kept out of it,' said Scott to himself, after a glance. 'We'll have cholera, sure as a gun, when the Rains come.'

But William seemed to have taken kindly to the operations of the Famine Code, which, when famine is declared, supersede the workings of the ordinary law. Scott saw her, the centre of a mob of weeping women, in a calico riding-habit and a blue-gray felt hat with a gold puggaree.

'I want fifty rupees, please. I forgot to ask Jack before he went away. Can you lend it me? It's for condensed milk for the babies,' said she.

Scott took the money from his belt, and handed it over without a word. 'For goodness sake take care of yourself,' he said.

'Oh, I shall be all right. We ought to get the milk in two days. By the way, the orders are, I was to tell you, that you're to take one of Sir Jim's horses. There's a gray Cabuli here that I thought would be just your style, so I've said you'd take him. Was that right?'

'That's awfully good of you. We can't either of us talk much about style, I'm afraid.'

Scott was in a weather-stained drill shooting-kit, very white at the seams and a little frayed at the wrists. William regarded him thoughtfully, from his pith helmet to his greased ankle-boots. 'You look very nice, I think. Are you sure you've everything you'll need—quinine, chlorodyne, and so on?'

'Think so,' said Scott, patting three or four of his shooting pockets as the horse was led up, and he mounted and rode alongside his convoy.

'Good-bye,' he cried.

'Good-bye, and good luck,' said William. 'I'm awfully obliged for the money.' She turned on a spurred heel and disappeared into the tent, while the carts pushed on past the famine-sheds, past the roaring lines of the thick, fat fires, down to the baked Gehenna of the South.

WILLIAM THE CONQUEROR

PART II

So let us melt and make no noise,
  No tear-floods nor sigh-tempests move;
'Twere profanation of our joys
  To tell the laity our love.
                A VALEDICTION.

IT was punishing work, even though he travelled by night and camped by day; but within the limits of his vision there was no man whom Scott could call master. He was as free as Jimmy Hawkins—freer, in fact, for the Government held the Head of the Famine tied neatly to a telegraph-wire, and if Jimmy had ever regarded telegrams seriously, the death-rate of that famine would have been much higher than it was.

At the end of a few days' crawling Scott learned something of the size of the India which he served; and it astonished him. His carts, as you know, were loaded with wheat, millet, and barley, good food-grains needing only a little grinding. But the people to whom he brought the life-giving stuffs were rice eaters. They knew how to hull rice in their mortars, but they knew nothing of the heavy stone querns of the North, and less of the material that the white man convoyed so laboriously. They clamoured for rice—unhusked paddy, such as they were accustomed to—and, when they found that there was none, broke away weeping from the sides of the cart. What was the use of these strange hard grains that choked their throats? They would die. And then and there were many of them kept their word. Others took their allowance, and bartered enough millet to feed a man through a week for a few handfuls of rotten rice saved by some less unfortunate. A few put their shares into the rice-mortars, pounded it, and made a paste with foul water; but they were very few. Scott understood dimly that many people in the India of the South ate rice, as a rule, but he had spent his service in a grain Province, had seldom seen rice in the blade or the ear, and least of all would have believed that, in time of deadly need, men would die at arm's length of plenty, sooner than touch food they did not know. In vain the interpreters interpreted; in vain his two policemen showed by vigorous pantomime what should be done. The starving crept away to their bark and weeds, grubs, leaves, and clay, and left the open sacks untouched. But sometimes the women laid their phantoms of children at Scott's feet, looking back as they staggered away.

Faiz Ullah opined it was the will of God that these foreigners should die, and therefore it remained only to give orders to burn the dead. None the less there was no reason why the Sahib should lack his comforts, and Faiz Ullah, a campaigner of experience, had picked up a few lean goats and had added them to the procession. That they might give milk for the morning meal, he was feeding them on the good grain that these imbeciles rejected. 'Yes,' said Faiz Ullah; 'if the Sahib thought fit, a little milk might be given to some of the babies'; but, as the Sahib well knew, babies were cheap, and, for his own part, Faiz Ullah held that there was no Government order as to babies. Scott spoke forcefully to Faiz Ullah and the two policemen, and bade them capture goats where they could find them. This they most joyfully did, for it was a recreation, and many ownerless goats were driven in. Once fed, the poor brutes were willing enough to follow the carts, and a few days' good food—food such as human beings died for lack of—set them in milk again.

'But I am no goatherd,' said Faiz Ullah. 'It is against my *izzat* [my honour].'

'When we cross the Bias River again we will talk of *izzat*,' Scott replied. 'Till that day thou and the policemen shall be sweepers to the camp, if I give the order.'

'Thus, then, it is done,' grunted Faiz Ullah, 'if the Sahib will have it so'; and he showed how a goat should be milked, while Scott stood over him.

'Now we will feed them,' said Scott; 'thrice a day we will feed them'; and he bowed his back to the milking, and took a horrible cramp.

When you have to keep connection unbroken between a restless mother of kids and a baby who is at the point of death, you suffer in all your system. But the babies were fed. Morning, noon and evening Scott would solemnly lift them out one by one from their nest of gunny-bags under the cart-tilts. There were always many who could do no more than breathe, and the milk was dropped into their toothless mouths drop by drop, with due pauses when they choked. Each morning, too, the goats were fed; and since they would struggle without a leader, and since the natives were hirelings, Scott was forced to give up riding, and pace slowly at the head of his flocks, accommodating his step to their weaknesses. All this was sufficiently absurd, and he felt the absurdity keenly; but at least he was saving life, and when the women saw that their children did not die, they made shift to eat a little of the strange foods, and crawled after the carts, blessing the master of the goats.

'Give the women something to live for,' said Scott to

himself, as he sneezed in the dust of a hundred little feet, 'and they'll hang on somehow. But this beats William's condensed milk trick all to pieces. I shall never live it down, though.'

He reached his destination very slowly, found that a rice-ship had come in from Burmah, and that stores of paddy were available; found also an overworked Englishman in charge of the shed, and, loading the carts, set back to cover the ground he had already passed. He left some of the children and half his goats at the famine-shed. For this he was not thanked by the Englishman, who had already more stray babies than he knew what to do with. Scott's back was suppled to stooping now, and he went on with his wayside ministrations in addition to distributing the paddy. More babies and more goats were added unto him; but now some of the babies wore rags, and beads round their wrists or necks. '*That*,' said the interpreter, as though Scott did not know, 'signifies that their mothers hope in eventual contingency to resume them offeecially.'

'The sooner the better,' said Scott; but at the same time he marked, with the pride of ownership, how this or that little Ramasawmy was putting on flesh like a bantam. As the paddy carts were emptied he headed for Hawkins's camp by the railway, timing his arrival to fit in with the dinner-hour, for it was long since he had eaten at a cloth. He had no desire to make any dramatic entry, but an accident of the sunset ordered it that, when he had taken off his helmet to get the evening breeze, the low light should fall across his forehead, and he could not see what was before him; while one waiting at the tent door beheld, with new eyes, a young man, beautiful as Paris, a god in a halo of golden dust, walking slowly at the head of his flocks, while at his knee ran small naked Cupids. But she laughed—William, in a slate-coloured blouse, laughed consumedly till Scott, putting the best face he could upon the matter, halted his armies and bade her admire the kindergarten. It was an unseemly sight, but the proprieties had been left ages ago, with the tea-party at Amritsar Station, fifteen hundred miles to the northward.

'They are coming on nicely,' said William. 'We've only five-and-twenty here now. The women are beginning to take them away again.'

'Are you in charge of the babies, then?'

'Yes—Mrs. Jim and I. We didn't think of goats, though. We've been trying condensed milk and water.'

'Any losses?'

'More than I care to think of,' said William, with a shudder. 'And you?'

Scott said nothing. There had been many little burials along his route—many mothers who had wept when they did not find again the children they had trusted to the care of the Government.

Then Hawkins came out carrying a razor, at which Scott looked hungrily, for he had a beard that he did not love. And when they sat down to dinner in the tent he told his tale in few words, as it might have been an official report. Mrs. Jim snuffled from time to time, and Jim bowed his head judicially; but William's gray eyes were on the clean-shaven face, and it was to her that Scott seemed to speak.

'Good for the Pauper Province!' said William, her chin in her hand, as she leaned forward among the wine-glasses. Her cheeks had fallen in, and the scar on her forehead was more prominent than ever, but the well-turned neck rose roundly as a column from the ruffle of the blouse which was the accepted evening-dress in camp.

'It was awfully absurd at times,' said Scott. 'You see I didn't know much about milking or babies. They'll chaff my head off, if the tale goes north.'

'Let 'em,' said William, haughtily. 'We've all done

coolie work since we came. I know Jack has.' This was to Hawkins's address, and the big man smiled blandly.

'Your brother's a highly efficient officer, William,' said he, and I've done him the honour of treating him as he deserves. Remember, I write the confidential reports.'

'Then you must say that William's worth her weight in gold,' said Mrs. Jim. 'I don't know what we should have done without her. She has been everything to us.' She dropped her hand upon William's, which was rough with much handling of reins, and William patted it softly. Jim beamed on the company. Things were going well with his world. Three of his more grossly incompetent men had died, and their places had been filled by their betters. Every day brought the rains nearer. They had put out the famine in five of the Eight Districts, and, after all, the death-rate had not been too heavy—things considered. He looked Scott over carefully, as an ogre looks over a man, and rejoiced in his thews and iron hard condition.

'He's just the least bit in the world tucked up,' said Jim to himself, 'but he can do two men's work yet.' Then he was aware that Mrs. Jim was telegraphing to him, and according to the domestic code the message ran: 'A clear case. Look at them!'

He looked and listened. All that William was saying was: 'What can you expect of a country where they call a *bhistee* [a water-carrier] a *tunni-cutch?*' and all that Scott answered was: 'I shall be precious glad to get back to the Club. Save me a dance at the Christmas ball, won't you?'

'It's a far cry from here to the Lawrence Hall,' said Jim. 'Better turn in early, Scott. It's paddy-carts to-morrow; you'll begin loading at five.'

'Aren't you going to give Mr. Scott one day's rest?'

'Wish I could, Lizzie. 'Fraid I can't. As long as he can stand up we must use him.'

'Well, I've had one Europe evening, at least . . . By

Jove, I'd nearly forgotten! What do I do about those babies of mine?'

'Leave them here,' said William—'we are in charge of that—and as many goats as you can spare. I must learn how to milk now.'

'If you care to get up early enough to-morrow I'll show you. I have to milk, you see; and, by the way, half of 'em have beads and things round their necks. You must be careful not to take 'em off, in case the mothers turn up.'

'You forget I've had some experience here.'

'I hope to goodness you won't overdo.' Scott's voice was unguarded.

'I'll take care of her,' said Mrs. Jim, telegraphing hundred-word messages as she carried William off, while Jim gave Scott his orders for the coming campaign. It was very late—nearly nine o'clock.

'Jim, you're a brute,' said his wife, that night; and the Head of the Famine chuckled.

'Not a bit of it, dear I remember doing the first Jandiala Settlement for the sake of a girl in a crinoline; and she was slender, Lizzie. I've never done as good a piece of work since. *He*'ll work like a demon.'

'But you might have given him one day.'

'And let things come to a head now? No, dear; it's their happiest time.'

'I don't believe either of the dears know what's the matter with them. Isn't it beautiful? Isn't it lovely?'

'Getting up at three to learn to milk, bless her heart! Ye gods, why must we grow old and fat?'

'She's a darling. She has done more work under me—'

'Under *you!* The day after she came she was in charge and you were her subordinate, and you've stayed there ever since. She manages you almost as well as you manage me.'

'She doesn't, and that's why I love her. She's as direct as a man—as her brother.'

'Her brother's weaker than she is. He's always coming to me for orders; but he's honest, and a glutton for work. I confess I'm rather fond of William, and if I had a daughter—'

The talk ended there. Far away in the Derajat was a child's grave more than twenty years old, and neither Jim nor his wife spoke of it any more.

'All the same, you're responsible,' Jim added, after a moment's silence.

'Bless 'em,' said Mrs. Jim, sleepily.

Before the stars paled, Scott, who slept in an empty cart, waked and went about his work in silence; it seemed at that hour unkind to rouse Faiz Ullah and the interpreter. His head being close to the ground, he did not hear William till she stood over him in the dingy old riding-habit, her eyes still heavy with sleep, a cup of tea and a piece of toast in her hands. There was a baby on the ground, squirming on a piece of blanket, and a six-year-old child peered over Scott's shoulder.

'Hai, you little rip,' said Scott, 'how the deuce do you expect to get your rations if you aren't quiet?'

A cool white hand steadied the brat, who forthwith choked as the milk gurgled into his mouth.

'Mornin',' said the milker. 'You've no notion how these little fellows can wriggle.'

'Oh, yes, I have.' She whispered, because the world was asleep. 'Only I feed them with a spoon or a rag. Yours are fatter than mine. . . . And you've been doing this day after day, twice a day?' The voice was almost lost.

'Yes; it was absurd. Now you try,' he said, giving place to the girl. 'Look out! A goat's not a cow.'

The goat protested against the amateur, and there was a scuffle, in which Scott snatched up the baby. Then it was all to do over again, and William laughed softly and merrily. She managed, however, to feed two babies, and a third.

'Don't the little beggars take it well!' said Scott. 'I trained 'em.'

They were very busy and interested, when, lo! it was broad daylight, and before they knew, the camp was awake, and they kneeled among the goats, surprised by the day, both flushed to the temples. Yet all the round world rolling up out of the darkness might have heard and seen all that had passed between them.

'Oh,' said William, unsteadily, snatching up the tea and toast, 'I had this made for you. It's stone-cold now. I thought you mightn't have anything ready so early. Better not drink it. It's—it's stone-cold.'

'That's awfully kind of you. It's just right. It's awfully good of you, really. I'll leave my kids and goats with you and Mrs. Jim; and, of course, any one in camp can show you about the milking.'

'Of course,' said William; and she grew pinker and pinker and statelier and more stately, as she strode back to her tent, fanning herself vigorously with the saucer.

There were shrill lamentations through the camp when the elder children saw their nurse move off without them. Faiz Ullah unbent so far as to jest with the policemen, and Scott turned purple with shame because Hawkins, already in the saddle, roared.

A child escaped from the care of Mrs. Jim, and, running like a rabbit, clung to Scott's boot, William pursuing with long, easy strides.

'I will not go—I will not go!' shrieked the child, twining his feet round Scott's ankle. 'They will kill me here. I do not know these people.'

'I say,' said Scott, in broken Tamil, 'I say, she will do you no harm. Go with her and be well fed.'

'Come!' said William, panting, with a wrathful glance

at Scott, who stood helpless and, as it were, hamstrung.

'Go back,' said Scott quickly to William. 'I'll send the little chap over in a minute.'

The tone of authority had its effect, but in a way Scott did not exactly intend. The boy loosened his grasp, and said with gravity, 'I did not know the woman was thine. I will go.' Then he cried to his companions, a mob of three-, four-, and five-year-olds waiting on the success of his venture ere they stampeded: 'Go back and eat. It is our man's woman. She will obey his orders.'

Jim collapsed where he sat; Faiz Ullah and the two policemen grinned; and Scott's orders to the cartmen flew like hail.

'That is the custom of the Sahibs when truth is told in their presence,' said Faiz Ullah. 'The time comes that I must seek new service. Young wives, especially such as speak our language and have knowledge of the ways of the Police, make great trouble for honest butlers in the matter of weekly accounts.'

What William thought of it all she did not say, but when her brother, ten days later, came to camp for orders, and heard of Scott's performances, he said, laughing: 'Well, that settles it. He'll be *Bakri* Scott to the end of his days (*Bakri*, in the northern vernacular, means a goat). 'What a lark! I'd have given a month's pay to have seen him nursing famine babies. I fed some with *conjee* [rice-water], but that was all right.'

'It's perfectly disgusting,' said his sister, with blazing eyes. 'A man does something like—like that—and all you other men think of is to give him an absurd nickname, and then you laugh and think it's funny.'

'Ah,' said Mrs. Jim, sympathetically.

'Well, *you* can't talk, William. You christened little Miss Demby the Button-quail last cold weather; you know you did. India's the land of nicknames.'

'That's different,' William replied. 'She was only a girl, and she hadn't done anything except walk like a quail, and she *does*. But it isn't fair to make fun of a man.'

'Scott won't care,' said Martyn. 'You can't get a rise out of old Scotty. I've been trying for eight years, and you've only known him for three. How does he look?'

'He looks very well,' said William, and went away with a flushed cheek. '*Bakri* Scott, indeed!' Then she laughed to herself, for she knew the country of her service. 'But it will be *Bakri* all the same'; and she repeated it under her breath several times slowly, whispering it into favour.

When he returned to his duties on the railway, Martyn spread the name far and wide among his associates, so that Scott met it as he led his paddy-carts to war. The natives believed it to be some English title of honour, and the cart-drivers used it in all simplicity till Faiz Ullah, who did not approve of foreign japes, broke their heads. There was very little time for milking now, except at the big camps, where Jim had extended Scott's idea, and was feeding large flocks on the useless northern grains. Enough paddy had come into the Eight Districts to hold the people safe, if it were only distributed quickly; and for that purpose no one was better than the big Canal officer, who never lost his temper, never gave an unnecessary order, and never questioned an order given. Scott pressed on, saving his cattle, washing their galled necks daily, so that no time should be lost on the road; reported himself with his rice at the minor famine-sheds, unloaded, and went back light by forced night-march to the next distributing centre, to find Hawkins's unvarying telegram: 'Do it again.' And he did it again and again, and yet again, while Jim Hawkins, fifty miles away, marked off on a big map the tracks of his wheels gridironing the stricken lands. Others did well—Hawkins reported at the end that they all did well—but Scott was the most excellent, for he kept good coined rupees by him, and paid for his own cart-repairs on the spot, and ran to meet all sorts of unconsidered extras, trusting to be recouped later. Theoretically, the Government should have paid for every shoe and linchpin, for every hand employed in the loading; but Government vouchers cash themselves slowly, and intelligent and efficient clerks write at great length, contesting unauthorised expenditures of eight annas. The man who wishes to make his work a success must draw on his own bank-account of money or other things as he goes.

'I told you he'd work,' said Jimmy to his wife at the end of six weeks. 'He's been in sole charge of a couple of thousand men up north on the Mosuhl Canal for a year, and he gives one less trouble than young Martyn with his ten constables; and I'm morally certain—only Government doesn't recognise moral obligations—that he's spent about half his pay to grease his wheels. Look at this, Lizzie, for one week's work! Forty miles in two days with twelve carts; two days' halt building a famine-shed for young Rogers (Rogers ought to have built it himself, the idiot!). Then forty miles back again, loading six carts on the way, and distributing all Sunday. Then in the evening he pitches in a twenty-page demi-official to me, saying that the people where he is might be "advantageously employed on relief-work," and suggesting that he put 'em to work on some broken-down old reservoir he's discovered, so as to have a good water-supply when the Rains come. He thinks he can caulk the dam in a fortnight. Look at his marginal sketches—aren't they clear and good? I knew he was *pukka*, but I didn't know he was as *pukka* as this!'

'I must show these to William,' said Mrs. Jim. 'The child's wearing herself out among the babies.'

'Not more than you are, dear. Well, another two months ought to see us out of the wood. I'm sorry it's not in my power to recommend you for a V.C.'

William sat late in her tent that night, reading through page after page of the square handwriting, patting the sketches of proposed repairs to the reservoir, and wrinkling her eyebrows over the columns of figures of estimated water-supply.

'And he finds time to do all this,' she cried to herself, 'and . . . well, I also was present. I've saved one or two babies.'

She dreamed for the twentieth time of the god in the golden dust, and woke refreshed to feed loathsome black children, scores of them, wastrels picked up by the wayside, their bones almost breaking their skin, terrible and covered with sores.

Scott was not allowed to leave his cart work, but his letter was duly forwarded to the Government, and he had the consolation, not rare in India, of knowing that another man was reaping where he had sown. That also was discipline profitable to the soul.

'He's much too good to waste on canals,' said Jimmy. 'Any one can oversee coolies. You needn't be angry, William: he can—but I need my pearl among bullock-drivers, and I've transferred him to the Khanda district, where he'll have it all to do over again. He should be marching now.'

'He's *not* a coolie,' said William furiously. 'He ought to be doing his regulation work.'

'He's the best man in his service, and that's saying a good deal; but if you *must* use razors to cut grindstones, why, I prefer the best cutlery.'

'Isn't it almost time we saw him again?' said Mrs. Jim. 'I'm sure the poor boy hasn't had a respectable meal for a month. He probably sits on a cart and eats sardines with his fingers.'

'All in good time, dear Duty before decency—wasn't it Mr. Chucks said that?'

'No; it was Midshipman Easy,' William laughed. 'I sometimes wonder how it will feel to dance or listen to a band again, or sit under a roof. I can't believe that I ever wore a ball-frock in my life.'

'One minute,' said Mrs. Jim, who was thinking. 'If he goes to Khanda, he passes within five miles of us. Of course he'll ride in.'

'Oh, no, he won't,' said William.

'How do you know, dear?'

'It'll take him off his work. He won't have time.'

'He'll make it,' said Mrs. Jim, with a twinkle.

'It depends on his own judgment. There's absolutely no reason why he shouldn't, if he thinks fit,' said Jim.

'He won't see fit,' William replied, without sorrow or emotion. 'It wouldn't be him if he did.'

'One certainly gets to know people rather well in times like these,' said Jim, drily; but William's face was serene as ever, and, even as she prophesied, Scott did not appear.

The Rains fell at last, late, but heavily; and the dry, gashed earth was red mud, and servants killed snakes in the camp, where every one was weather-bound for a fortnight—all except Hawkins, who took horse and splashed about in the wet, rejoicing. Now the Government decreed that seed-grain should be distributed to the people, as well as advances of money for the purchase of new oxen; and the white men were doubly worked for this new duty, while William skipped from brick to brick laid down on the trampled mud, and dosed her charges with warming medicines that made them rub their little round stomachs; and the milch-goats throve on the rank grass. There was never a word from Scott in the Khanda district, away to the south-east, except the regular telegraphic report to Hawkins. The rude country roads had disappeared; his drivers were half mutinous; one of Martyn's loaned policemen had died of cholera; and Scott was taking thirty grains of quinine a day to fight the fever that comes if one works hard in heavy rain; but those were things he did not consider necessary to report. He was, as usual, working from a base of supplies on a railway line, to cover a circle of fifteen miles radius, and since full loads were impossible, he took quarter-loads, and toiled four times as hard by consequence; for he did not choose to risk an epidemic which might have grown uncontrollable by assembling villagers in thousands at the relief-sheds. It was cheaper to take Government bullocks, work them to death, and leave them to the crows in the wayside sloughs.

That was the time when eight years of clean living and hard condition told, though a man's head were ringing like a bell from the cinchona, and the earth swayed under his feet when he stood and under his bed when he slept. If Hawkins had seen fit to make him a bullock-driver, that, he thought, was entirely Hawkins's own affair. There were men in the North who would know what he had done; men of thirty years' service in his own department who would say that it was 'not half bad'; and above, immeasurably above all men of all grades, there was William in the thick of the fight, who would approve because she understood. He had so trained his mind that it would hold fast to the mechanical routine of the day, though his own voice sounded strange in his own ears, and his hands, when he wrote, grew large as pillows or small as peas at the end of his wrists. That steadfastness bore his body to the telegraph-office at the railway-station, and dictated a telegram to Hawkins, saying that the Khanda district was, in his judgment, now safe, and he 'waited further orders.'

The Madrassee telegraph-clerk did not approve of a large, gaunt man falling over him in a dead faint, not so much because of the weight, as because of the names and blows that Faiz Ullah dealt him when he found the body rolled under a bench. Then Faiz Ullah took blankets and quilts and coverlets where he found them, and lay down under them at his master's side, and bound his arms with a tent-rope, and filled him with a horrible stew of herbs, and set the policeman to fight him when he wished to escape from the intolerable heat of his coverings, and shut the door of the telegraph-office to keep out the curious for two nights and one day; and when a light engine came down the line, and Hawkins kicked in the door, Scott hailed him weakly, but in a natural voice, and Faiz Ullah stood back and took all the credit.

'For two nights, Heaven-born, he was *pagal*,' said Faiz Ullah. 'Look at my nose, and consider the eye of the policeman. He beat us with his bound hands; but we sat upon him, Heaven-born, and though his words were *tez*, we sweated him. Heaven-born, never has been such a sweat! He is weaker now than a child; but the fever has gone out of him, by the grace of God. There remains only my nose and the eye of the constabeel. Sahib, shall I ask for my dismissal because my Sahib has beaten me?' And Faiz Ullah laid his long thin hand carefully on Scott's chest to be sure that the fever was all gone, ere he went out to open tinned soups and discourage such as laughed at his swelled nose.

'The district's all right,' Scott whispered. 'It doesn't make any difference. You got my wire? I shall be fit in a week. 'Can't understand how it happened. I shall be fit in a few days.'

'You're coming into camp with us,' said Hawkins.

'But look here—but—'

'It's all over except the shouting. We sha'n't need you Punjabis any more. On my honour, we sha'n't. Martyn goes back in a few weeks; Arbuthnot's returned already; Ellis and Clay are putting the last touches to a new feeder-line the Government's built as relief-work. Morten's dead —he was a Bengal man, though; you wouldn't know him.

'Pon my word, you and Will—Miss Martyn—seem to have come through it as well as anybody.'

'Oh, how is she?' The voice went up and down as he spoke.

'She was in great form when I left her. The Roman Catholic Missions are adopting the unclaimed babies to turn them into little priests; the Basil Mission is taking some, and the mothers are taking the rest. You should hear the little beggars howl when they're sent away from William. She's pulled down a bit, but so are we all. Now, when do you suppose you'll be able to move?'

'I can't come into camp in this state. I won't,' he replied pettishly.

'Well, you *are* rather a sight, but from what I gathered there it seemed to me they'd be glad to see you under any conditions. I'll look over your work here, if you like, for a couple of days, and you can pull yourself together while Faiz Ullah feeds you up.'

Scott could walk dizzily by the time Hawkins's inspection was ended, and he flushed all over when Jim said of his work in the district that it was 'not half bad,' and volunteered, further, that he had considered Scott his right-hand man through the famine, and would feel it his duty to say as much officially.

So they came back by rail to the old camp; but there were no crowds near it, the long fires in the trenches were dead and black, and the famine-sheds stood almost empty.

'You see!' said Jim. 'There isn't much more for us to do. Better ride up and see the wife. They've pitched a tent for you. Dinner's at seven. I'll see you then.'

Riding at a foot-pace, Faiz Ullah by his stirrup, Scott came to William in the brown-calico riding-habit, sitting at the dining-tent door, her hands in her lap, white as ashes, thin and worn, with no lustre in her hair. There did not seem to be any Mrs. Jim on the horizon, and all that

William could say was: 'My word, how pulled down you look!'

'I've had a touch of fever. You don't look very well yourself.'

'Oh, I'm fit enough. We've stamped it out. I suppose you know?'

Scott nodded. 'We shall all be returned in a few weeks. Hawkins told me.'

'Before Christmas, Mrs. Jim says. Sha'n't you be glad to go back? I can smell the wood-smoke already'; William sniffed. 'We shall be in time for all the Christmas doings. I don't suppose even the Punjab Government would be base enough to transfer Jack till the new year?'

'It seems hundreds of years ago—the Punjab and all that—doesn't it? Are you glad you came?'

'Now it's all over, yes. It has been ghastly here. You know we had to sit still and do nothing, and Sir Jim was away so much.'

'Do nothing! How did you get on with the milking?'

'I managed it somehow—after you taught me.'

Then the talk stopped with an almost audible jar. Still no Mrs. Jim.

'That reminds me I owe you fifty rupees for the condensed milk. I thought perhaps you'd be coming here when you were transferred to the Khanda district, and I could pay you then; but you didn't.'

'I passed within five miles of the camp. It was in the middle of a march, you see, and the carts were breaking down every few minutes, and I couldn't get 'em over the ground till ten o'clock that night. But I wanted to come awfully. You knew I did, didn't you?'

'I—believe—I—did,' said William, facing him with level eyes. She was no longer white.

'Did you understand?'

'Why you didn't ride in? Of course I did.'

'Why?'

'Because you couldn't of course. I knew that.'

'Did you care?'

'If you had come in—but I knew you wouldn't—but if you *had*, I should have cared a great deal. You know I should.'

'Thank God I didn't! Oh, but I wanted to! I couldn't trust myself to ride in front of the carts, because I kept edging 'em over here, don't you know?'

'I knew you wouldn't,' said William, contentedly. 'Here's your fifty.'

Scott bent forward and kissed the hand that held the greasy notes. Its fellow patted him awkwardly but very tenderly on the head.

'And *you* knew, too, didn't you?' said William, in a new voice.

'No, on my honour, I didn't. I hadn't the—the cheek to expect anything of the kind, except . . . I say, were you out riding anywhere the day I passed by to Khanda?'

William nodded, and smiled after the manner of an angel surprised in a good deed.

'Then it was just a speck I saw of your habit in the—'

'Palm-grove on the Southern cart-road. I saw your helmet when you came up from the nullah by the temple—just enough to be sure that you were all right. D'you care?'

This time Scott did not kiss her hand, for they were in the dusk of the dining-tent, and, because William's knees were trembling under her, she had to sit down in the nearest chair, where she wept long and happily, her head on her arms; and when Scott imagined that it would be well to comfort her, she needed nothing of the kind; she ran to her own tent; and Scott went out into the world, and smiled upon it largely and idiotically. But when Faiz

Ullah brought him a drink, he found it necessary to support one hand with the other, or the good whisky and soda would have been spilled abroad. There are fevers and fevers.

But it was worse—much worse—the strained, eye-shirking talk at dinner till the servants had withdrawn, and worst of all when Mrs. Jim, who had been on the edge of weeping from the soup down, kissed Scott and William, and they drank one whole bottle of champagne, hot, because there was no ice, and Scott and William sat outside the tent in the starlight till Mrs. Jim drove them in for fear of more fever.

Apropos of these things and some others William said: 'Being engaged is abominable, because, you see, one has no official position. We must be thankful that we've lots of things to do.'

'Things to do!' said Jim, when that was reported to him. 'They're neither of them any good any more. I can't get five hours' work a day out of Scott. He's in the clouds half the time.'

'Oh, but they're so beautiful to watch, Jimmy. It will break my heart when they go. Can't you do anything for him?'

'I've given the Government the impression—at least, I hope I have—that he personally conducted the entire famine. But all he wants is to get on to the Luni Canal Works, and William's just as bad. Have you ever heard 'em talking of barrage and aprons and wastewater. It's their style of spooning, I suppose.'

Mrs. Jim smiled tenderly. 'Ah, that's in the intervals—bless 'em.'

And so Love ran about the camp unrebuked in broad daylight, while men picked up the pieces and put them neatly away of the Famine in the Eight Districts.

* * * * *

Morning brought the penetrating chill of the Northern December, the layers of wood-smoke, the dusty gray blue of the tamarisks, the domes of ruined tombs, and all the smell of the white Northern plains, as the mail-train ran on to the mile-long Sutlej Bridge. William, wrapped in a *poshteen*—silk-embroidered sheepskin jacket trimmed with rough astrakhan—looked out with moist eyes and nostrils that dilated joyously. The South of pagodas and palm-trees, the over-populated Hindu South, was done with. Here was the land she knew and loved, and before her lay the good life she understood, among folk of her own caste and mind.

They were picking them up at almost every station now —men and women coming in for the Christmas Week, with racquets, with bundles of polo-sticks, with dear and bruised cricket-bats, with fox-terriers and saddles. The greater part of them wore jackets like William's, for the Northern cold is as little to be trifled with as the Northern heat. And William was among them and of them, her hands deep in her pockets, her collar turned up over her ears, stamping her feet on the platforms as she walked up and down to get warm, visiting from carriage to carriage, and everywhere being congratulated. Scott was with the bachelors at the far end of the train, where they chaffed him mercilessly about feeding babies and milking goats; but from time to time he would stroll up to William's window, and murmur: 'Good enough, isn't it?' and William would answer, with sighs of pure delight: 'Good enough, indeed.' The large open names of the home towns were good to listen to. Umballa, Ludianah, Phillour, Jullundur, they rang like the coming marriage-bells in her ears, and William felt deeply and truly sorry for all strangers and outsiders—visitors, tourists, and those fresh caught for the service of the country.

It was a glorious return, and when the bachelors gave

the Christmas ball, William was, unofficially, you might say, the chief and honoured guest among the stewards, who could make things very pleasant for their friends. She and Scott danced nearly all the dances together, and sat out the rest in the big dark gallery overlooking the superb teak floor, where the uniforms blazed, and the spurs clinked, and the new frocks and four hundred dancers went round and round till the draped flags on the pillars flapped and bellied to the whirl of it.

About midnight half a dozen men who did not care for dancing came over from the Club to play 'Waits,' and—that was a surprise the stewards had arranged—before any one knew what had happened, the band stopped, and hidden voices broke into 'Good King Wenceslaus,' and William in the gallery hummed and beat time with her foot:

> Mark my footsteps well, my page,
> Tread thou in them boldly,
> Thou shalt feel the winter's rage
> Freeze thy blood less coldly!

'Oh, I hope they are going to give us another! Isn't it pretty, coming out of the dark in that way? Look—look down. There's Mrs. Gregory wiping her eyes!'

'It's like home, rather,' said Scott. 'I remember—

'H'sh! Listen!—dear.' And it began again:

> When shepherds watched their flocks by night—

'A-h-h!' said William, drawing closer to Scott.

> All seated on the ground,
> The Angel of the Lord came down,
> And glory shone around.
> 'Fear not,' said he (for mighty dread
> Had seized their troubled mind);
> 'Glad tidings of great joy I bring
> To you and all mankind.'

This time it was William that wiped her eyes.

WEE WILLIE WINKIE

AN OFFICER AND A GENTLEMAN

HIS full name was Percival William Williams, but he picked up the other name in a nursery-book, and that was the end of the christened titles. His mother's *ayah* called him Willie-*Baba*, but as he never paid the faintest attention to anything that the *ayah* said, her wisdom did not help matters.

His father was the Colonel of the 195th, and as soon as Wee Willie Winkie was old enough to understand what Military Discipline meant, Colonel Williams put him under it. There was no other way of managing the child. When he was good for a week, he drew good-conduct pay; and when he was bad, he was deprived of his good-conduct stripe. Generally he was bad, for India offers many chances of going wrong to little six-year-olds.

Children resent familiarity from strangers, and Wee Willie Winkie was a very particular child. Once he accepted an acquaintance, he was graciously pleased to thaw. He accepted Brandis, a subaltern of the 195th, on sight. Brandis was having tea at the Colonel's, and Wee Willie Winkie entered strong in the possession of a good-conduct badge won for not chasing the hens round the compound. He regarded Brandis with gravity for at least ten minutes, and then delivered himself of his opinion.

'I like you,' said he slowly, getting off his chair and coming over to Brandis. 'I like you. I shall call you Coppy, because of your hair. Do you *mind* being called Coppy? It is because of ve hair, you know.'

Here was one of the most embarrassing of Wee Willie Winkie's peculiarities. He would look at a stranger for some time, and then, without warning or explanation, would give him a name. And the name stuck. No regimental penalties could break Wee Willie Winkie of this habit. He lost his good-conduct badge for christening the Commissioner's wife 'Pobs'; but nothing that the Colonel could do made the Station forego the nickname, and Mrs. Collen remained 'Pobs' till the end of her stay. So Brandis was christened 'Coppy,' and rose, therefore, in the estimation of the regiment.

If Wee Willie Winkie took an interest in any one, the fortunate man was envied alike by the mess and the rank and file. And in their envy lay no suspicion of self-interest 'The Colonel's son' was idolised on his own merits entirely. Yet Wee Willie Winkie was not lovely. His face was permanently freckled, as his legs were permanently scratched, and in spite of his mother's almost tearful remonstrances he had insisted upon having his long yellow locks cut short in the military fashion. 'I want my hair like Sergeant Tummil's,' said Wee Willie Winkie, and, his father abetting, the sacrifice was accomplished.

Three weeks after the bestowal of his youthful affections on Lieutenant Brandis—henceforward to be called 'Coppy' for the sake of brevity—Wee Willie Winkie was destined to behold strange things and far beyond his comprehension.

Coppy returned his liking with interest. Coppy had let him wear for five rapturous minutes his own big sword—just as tall as Wee Willie Winkie. Coppy had promised him a terrier puppy; and Coppy had permitted him to witness the miraculous operation of shaving. Nay, more—

Coppy had said that even he, Wee Willie Winkie, would rise in time to the ownership of a box of shiny knives, a silver soap-box, and a silver-handled 'sputter-brush,' as Wee Willie Winkie called it. Decidedly, there was no one except his father, who could give or take away good-conduct badges at pleasure, half so wise, strong, and valiant as Coppy with the Afghan and Egyptian medals on his breast. Why, then, should Coppy be guilty of the unmanly weakness of kissing—vehemently kissing—a 'big girl,' Miss Allardyce to wit? In the course of a morning ride, Wee Willie Winkie had seen Coppy so doing, and, like the gentleman he was, had promptly wheeled round and cantered back to his groom, lest the groom should also see.

Under ordinary circumstances he would have spoken to his father, but he felt instinctively that this was a matter on which Coppy ought first to be consulted.

'Coppy,' shouted Wee Willie Winkie, reining up outside that subaltern's bungalow early one morning—'I want to see you, Coppy!'

'Come in, young 'un,' returned Coppy, who was at early breakfast in the midst of his dogs. 'What mischief have you been getting into now?'

Wee Willie Winkie had done nothing notoriously bad for three days, and so stood on a pinnacle of virtue.

'*I've* been doing nothing bad,' said he, curling himself into a long chair with a studious affectation of the Colonel's languor after a hot parade. He buried his freckled nose in a tea-cup and, with eyes staring roundly over the rim, asked: 'I say, Coppy, is it pwoper to kiss big girls?'

'By Jove! You're beginning early. Who do you want to kiss?'

'No one. My muvver's always kissing me if I don't stop her. If it isn't pwoper, how was you kissing Major Allardyce's big girl last morning, by ve canal?'

Coppy's brow wrinkled. He and Miss Allardyce had

with great craft managed to keep their engagement secret for a fortnight. There were urgent and imperative reasons why Major Allardyce should not know how matters stood for at least another month, and this small marplot had discovered a great deal too much.

'I saw you,' said Wee Willie Winkie calmly. 'But ve *sais* didn't see. I said, "*Hut jao!*"'

'Oh, you had that much sense, you young Rip,' groaned poor Coppy, half amused and half angry. 'And how many people may you have told about it?'

'Only me myself. You didn't tell when I twied to wide ve buffalo ven my pony was lame; and I fought you wouldn't like.'

'Winkie,' said Coppy enthusiastically, shaking the small hand, 'you're the best of good fellows. Look here, you can't understand all these things. One of these days—hang it, how can I make you see it!—I'm going to marry Miss Allardyce, and then she'll be Mrs. Coppy, as you say. If your young mind is so scandalised at the idea of kissing big girls, go and tell your father.'

'What will happen?' said Wee Willie Winkie, who firmly believed that his father was omnipotent.

'I shall get into trouble,' said Coppy, playing his trump card with an appealing look at the holder of the ace.

'Ven I won't,' said Wee Willie Winkie briefly. 'But my faver says it's un-man-ly to be always kissing, and I didn't fink *you'd* do vat, Coppy.'

'I'm not always kissing, old chap. It's only now and then, and when you're bigger you'll do it too. Your father meant it's not good for little boys.'

'Ah!' said Wee Willie Winkie, now fully enlightened. 'It's like ve sputter-brush?'

'Exactly,' said Coppy gravely.

'But I don't fink I'll ever want to kiss big girls, nor no one, 'cept my muvver. And I *must* vat, you know.'

There was a long pause, broken by Wee Willie Winkie.

'Are you fond of vis big girl, Coppy?'

'Awfully!' said Coppy.

'Fonder van you are of Bell or ve Butcha—or me?'

'It's in a different way,' said Coppy. 'You see, one of these days Miss Allardyce will belong to me, but you'll grow up and command the Regiment and—all sorts of things. It's quite different, you see.'

'Very well,' said Wee Willie Winkie, rising. 'If you're fond of ve big girl, I won't tell any one. I must go now.'

Coppy rose and escorted his small guest to the door, adding—'You're the best of little fellows, Winkie. I tell you what. In thirty days from now you can tell if you like—tell any one you like.'

Thus the secret of the Brandis-Allardyce engagement was dependent on a little child's word. Coppy, who knew Wee Willie Winkie's idea of truth, was at ease, for he felt that he would not break promises. Wee Willie Winkie betrayed a special and unusual interest in Miss Allardyce, and, slowly revolving round that embarrassed young lady, was used to regard her gravely with unwinking eye. He was trying to discover why Coppy should have kissed her. She was not half so nice as his own mother. On the other hand, she was Coppy's property, and would in time belong to him. Therefore it behoved him to treat her with as much respect as Coppy's big sword or shiny pistol.

The idea that he shared a great secret in common with Coppy kept Wee Willie Winkie unusually virtuous for three weeks. Then the Old Adam broke out, and he made what he called a 'camp-fire' at the bottom of the garden. How could he have foreseen that the flying sparks would have lighted the Colonel's little hay-rick and consumed a week's store for the horses? Sudden and swift was the punishment—deprivation of the good-conduct badge and, most sorrowful of all, two days' confinement to barracks—

the house and veranda—coupled with the withdrawal of the light of his father's countenance.

He took the sentence like the man he strove to be, drew himself up with a quivering under-lip, saluted, and, once clear of the room ran, to weep bitterly in his nursery—called by him 'my quarters.' Coppy came in the afternoon and attempted to console the culprit.

'I'm under awwest,' said Wee Willie Winkie mournfully, 'and I didn't ought to speak to you.'

Very early the next morning he climbed on to the roof of the house—that was not forbidden—and beheld Miss Allardyce going for a ride.

'Where are you going?' cried Wee Willie Winkie.

'Across the river,' she answered, and trotted forward.

Now the cantonment in which the 195th lay was bounded on the north by a river—dry in the winter. From his earliest years, Wee Willie Winkie had been forbidden to go across the river, and had noted that even Coppy—the almost almighty Coppy—had never set foot beyond it. Wee Willie Winkie had once been read to, out of a big blue book, the history of the Princess and the Goblins—a most wonderful tale of a land where the Goblins were always warring with the children of men until they were defeated by one Curdie. Ever since that date it seemed to him that the bare black and purple hills across the river were inhabited by Goblins, and, in truth, every one had said that there lived the Bad Men. Even in his own house the lower halves of the windows were covered with green paper on account of the Bad Men who might, if allowed clear view, fire into peaceful drawing-rooms and comfortable bedrooms. Certainly, beyond the river, which was the end of all the Earth, lived the Bad Men. And here was Major Allardyce's big girl, Coppy's property, preparing to venture into their borders! What would Coppy say if anything happened to her? If the Goblins ran off with her as they did with

Curdie's Princess? She must at all hazards be turned back.

The house was still. Wee Willie Winkie reflected for a moment on the very terrible wrath of his father; and then —broke his arrest! It was a crime unspeakable. The low sun threw his shadow, very large and very black, on the trim garden-paths, as he went down to the stables and ordered his pony. It seemed to him in the hush of the dawn that all the big world had been bidden to stand still and look at Wee Willie Winkie guilty of mutiny. The drowsy *sais* gave him his mount, and, since the one great sin made all others insignificant, Wee Willie Winkie said that he was going to ride over to Coppy Sahib, and went out at a foot-pace, stepping on the soft mould of the flower-borders.

The devastating track of the pony's feet was the last misdeed that cut him off from all sympathy of Humanity. He turned into the road, leaned forward, and rode as fast as the pony could put foot to the ground in the direction of the river.

But the liveliest of twelve-two ponies can do little against the long canter of a Waler. Miss Allardyce was far ahead, had passed through the crops, beyond the Police-posts, when all the guards were asleep, and her mount was scattering the pebbles of the river-bed as Wee Willie Winkie left the cantonment and British India behind him. Bowed forward and still flogging, Wee Willie Winkie shot into Afghan territory, and could just see Miss Allardyce a black speck, flickering across the stony plain. The reason of her wandering was simple enough. Coppy, in a tone of too-hastily-assumed authority, had told her overnight that she must not ride out by the river. And she had gone to prove her own spirit and teach Coppy a lesson.

Almost at the foot of the inhospitable hills, Wee Willie Winkie saw the Waler blunder and come down heavily.

Miss Allardyce struggled clear, but her ankle had been severely twisted, and she could not stand. Having fully shown her spirit, she wept, and was surprised by the apparition of a white, wide-eyed child in khaki, on a nearly spent pony.

'Are you badly, badly hurted?' shouted Wee Willie Winkie, as soon as he was within range. 'You didn't ought to be here.'

'I don't know,' said Miss Allardyce ruefully, ignoring the reproof. 'Good gracious, child, what are *you* doing here?'

'You said you was going acwoss ve wiver,' panted Wee Willie Winkie, throwing himself off his pony. 'And nobody—not even Coppy—must go acwoss ve wiver, and I came after you ever so hard, but you wouldn't stop, and now you've hurted yourself, and Coppy will be angwy wiv me, and—I've bwoken my awwest! I've bwoken my awwest!'

The future Colonel of the 195th sat down and sobbed. In spite of the pain in her ankle the girl was moved.

'Have you ridden all the way from cantonments, little man? What for?'

'You belonged to Coppy. Coppy told me so!' wailed Wee Willie Winkie disconsolately. 'I saw him kissing you, and he said he was fonder of you van Bell or ve Butcha or me. And so I came. You must get up and come back. You didn't ought to be here. Vis is a bad place, and I've bwoken my awwest.'

'I can't move, Winkie,' said Miss Allardyce, with a groan. 'I've hurt my foot. What shall I do?'

She showed a readiness to weep anew, which steadied Wee Willie Winkie, who had been brought up to believe that tears were the depth of unmanliness. Still, when one is as great a sinner as Wee Willie Winkie, even a man may be permitted to break down.

'Winkie,' said Miss Allardyce, 'when you've rested a little, ride back and tell them to send out something to carry me back in. It hurts fearfully.'

The child sat still for a little time and Miss Allardyce closed her eyes; the pain was nearly making her faint. She was roused by Wee Willie Winkie tying up the reins on his pony's neck and setting it free with a vicious cut of his whip that made it whicker. The little animal headed towards the cantonments.

'Oh, Winkie, what are you doing?'

'Hush!' said Wee Willie Winkie. 'Vere's a man coming —one of ve Bad Men. I must stay wiv you. My faver says a man must *always* look after a girl. Jack will go home, and ven vey'll come and look for us. Vat's why I let him go.'

Not one man but two or three had appeared from behind the rocks of the hills, and the heart of Wee Willie Winkie sank within him, for just in this manner were the Goblins wont to steal out and vex Curdie's soul. Thus had they played in Curdie's garden—he had seen the picture—and thus had they frightened the Princess's nurse. He heard them talking to each other, and recognised with joy the bastard Pushto that he had picked up from one of his father's grooms lately dismissed. People who spoke that tongue could not be the Bad Men. They were only natives after all.

They came up to the boulders on which Miss Allardyce's horse had blundered.

Then rose from the rock Wee Willie Winkie, child of the Dominant Race, aged six and three-quarters, and said briefly and emphatically '*Jao*!' The pony had crossed the river-bed.

The men laughed, and laughter from natives was the one thing Wee Willie Winkie could not tolerate. He asked them what they wanted and why they did not depart.

Other men with most evil faces and crooked-stocked guns crept out of the shadows of the hills, till, soon, Wee Willie Winkie was face to face with an audience some twenty strong. Miss Allardyce screamed.

'Who are you?' said one of the men.

'I am the Colonel Sahib's son, and my order is that you go at once. You black men are frightening the Miss Sahib. One of you must run into cantonments and take the news that the Miss Sahib has hurt herself, and that the Colonel's son is here with her.'

'Put our feet into the trap?' was the laughing reply. 'Hear this boy's speech!'

'Say that I sent you—I, the Colonel's son. They will give you money.'

'What is the use of this talk? Take up the child and the girl, and we can at least ask for the ransom. Ours are the villages on the heights,' said a voice in the background.

These *were* the Bad Men—worse than Goblins—and it needed all Wee Willie Winkie's training to prevent him from bursting into tears. But he felt that to cry before a native, excepting only his mother's *ayah*, would be an infamy greater than any mutiny. Moreover, he, as future Colonel of the 195th, had that grim regiment at his back.

'Are you going to carry us away?' said Wee Willie Winkie, very blanched and uncomfortable.

'Yes, my little *Sahib Bahadur*,' said the tallest of the men, 'and eat you afterwards.'

'That is child's talk,' said Wee Willie Winkie. 'Men do not eat men.'

A yell of laughter interrupted him, but he went on firmly —'And if you do carry us away, I tell you that all my regiment will come up in a day and kill you all without leaving one. Who will take my message to the Colonel Sahib?'

Speech in any vernacular—and Wee Willie Winkie had a colloquial acquaintance with three—was easy to the boy who could not yet manage his 'r's' and 'th's' aright.

Another man joined the conference, crying: 'O foolish men! What this babe says is true. He is the heart's heart of those white troops. For the sake of peace let them go both, for if he be taken, the regiment will break loose and gut the valley. *Our* villages are in the valley, and we shall not escape. That regiment are devils. They broke Khoda Yar's breastbone with kicks when he tried to take the rifles; and if we touch this child they will fire and rape and plunder for a month, till nothing remains. Better to send a man back to take the message and get a reward. I say that this child is their God, and that they will spare none of us, nor our women, if we harm him.'

It was Din Mahommed, the dismissed groom of the Colonel, who made the diversion, and an angry and heated discussion followed. Wee Willie Winkie, standing over Miss Allardyce, waited the upshot. Surely his 'wegiment,' his own 'wegiment,' would not desert him if they knew of his extremity.

* * * * *

The riderless pony brought the news to the 195th, though there had been consternation in the Colonel's household for an hour before. The little beast came in through the parade-ground in front of the main barracks, where the men were settling down to play Spoil-five till the afternoon. Devlin, the Colour-Sergeant of E Company, glanced at the empty saddle and tumbled through the barrack-rooms, kicking up each Room Corporal as he passed. 'Up, ye beggars! There's something happened to the Colonel's son,' he shouted.

'He couldn't fall off! S'elp me, 'e *couldn't* fall off,' blubbered a drummer boy. 'Go an' hunt acrost the river. He's over there if he's anywhere, an' maybe those Pathans have got 'im. For the love o' Gawd don't look for 'im in the nullahs! Let's go over the river.'

'There's sense in Mott yet,' said Devlin. 'E Company, double out to the river—sharp!'

So E Company, in its shirt-sleeves mainly, doubled for the dear life, and in the rear toiled the perspiring Sergeant, adjuring it to double yet faster. The cantonment was alive with the men of the 195th hunting for Wee Willie Winkie, and the Colonel finally overtook E Company, far too exhausted to swear, struggling in the pebbles of the river-bed.

Up the hill under which Wee Willie Winkie's Bad Men were discussing the wisdom of carrying off the child and the girl, a look-out fired two shots.

'What have I said?' shouted Din Mahommed. 'There is the warning! The *pulton* are out already and are coming across the plain! Get away! Let us not be seen with the boy!'

The men waited for an instant, and then, as another shot was fired, withdrew into the hills, silently as they had appeared.

'The wegiment is coming,' said Wee Willie Winkie confidently to Miss Allardyce, 'and it's all wight. Don't cwy!'

He needed the advice himself, for ten minutes later, when his father came up, he was weeping bitterly with his head in Miss Allardyce's lap.

And the men of the 195th carried him home with shouts and rejoicings; and Coppy, who had ridden a horse into a lather, met him, and, to his intense disgust, kissed him openly in the presence of the men.

But there was balm for his dignity. His father assured him that not only would the breaking of arrest be condoned, but that the good-conduct badge would be restored as soon as his mother could sew it on his blouse-sleeve. Miss Allardyce had told the Colonel a story that made him proud of his son.

'She belonged to you, Coppy,' said Wee Willie Winkie, indicating Miss Allardyce with a grimy forefinger. 'I *knew* she didn't ought to go acwoss ve wiver, and I knew ve wegiment would come to me if I sent Jack home.'

'You're a hero, Winkie,' said Coppy—'a *pukka* hero!'

'I don't know what vat means,' said Wee Willie Winkie, 'but you mustn't call me Winkie any no more. I'm Percival Will'am Will'ams.'

And in this manner did Wee Willie Winkie enter into his manhood.

A MATTER OF FACT.

And if ye doubt the tale I tell,
Steer through the South Pacific swell;
Go where the branching coral hives
Unending strife of endless lives,
Where, leagued about the 'wildered boat,
The rainbow jellies fill and float;
And, lilting where the laver lingers,
The starfish trips on all her fingers;
Where, 'neath his myriad spines ashock,
The sea-egg ripples down the rock;
An orange wonder dimly guessed,
From darkness where the cuttles rest,
Moored o'er the darker deeps that hide
The blind white Sea-snake and his bride
Who, drowsing, nose the long-lost ships
Let down through darkness to their lips.

The Palms.

ONCE a priest, always a priest; once a mason, always a mason; but once a journalist, always and for ever a journalist.

There were three of us, all newspaper men, the only passengers on a little tramp steamer that ran where her owners told her to go. She had once been in the Bilbao iron ore business, had been lent to the Spanish Government for service at Manilla; and was ending her days in the Cape Town coolie-trade, with occasional trips to Madagascar and even as far as England. We found her going to Southampton in ballast, and shipped in her because the fares were nominal. There was Keller, of an American paper, on his way back to the States from palace executions in Madagascar; there was a burly half-Dutchman, called Zuyland, who owned and edited a paper up country near Johannesburg; and there was myself, who had solemnly put away all journalism, vowing to forget that I had ever known the difference between an imprint and a stereo advertisement.

Ten minutes after Keller spoke to me, as the *Rathmines* cleared Cape Town, I had forgotten the aloofness I desired to feign, and was in heated discussion on the immorality of expanding telegrams beyond a certain fixed point. Then Zuyland came out of his cabin, and we were all at home instantly, because we were men of the same profession needing no introduction. We annexed the boat formally, broke open the passengers' bath-room door—on the Manilla lines the Dons do not wash—cleaned out the orange-peel and cigar-ends at the bottom of the bath, hired a Lascar to shave us throughout the voyage, and then asked each other's names.

Three ordinary men would have quarrelled through sheer boredom before they reached Southampton. We, by virtue of our craft, were anything but ordinary men. A large percentage of the tales of the world, the thirty-nine that cannot be told to ladies and the one that can, are common property coming of a common stock. We told them all, as a matter of form, with all their local and specific variants which are surprising. Then came, in the intervals of steady card-play, more personal histories of adventure and things seen and suffered: panics among white folk, when the blind terror ran from man to man on the Brooklyn Bridge, and the people crushed each other to death they knew not why; fires, and faces that opened and shut their mouths horribly at red-hot window frames; wrecks in frost and snow, reported from the sleet-sheathed rescue-tug at the risk of frost-bite; long rides after diamond thieves; skirmishes on the veldt and in municipal committees with the Boers; glimpses of lazy tangled Cape politics and the mule-rule in the Transvaal; card-tales, horse-tales, woman-tales, by the score and the half hundred; till the first mate, who had seen more than us all put together, but lacked words to clothe his tales with, sat open-mouthed far into the dawn.

When the tales were done we picked up cards till a curious hand or a chance remark made one or other of us say, 'That reminds me of a man who—or a business which—' and the anecdotes would continue while the *Rathmines* kicked her way northward through the warm water.

In the morning of one specially warm night we three were sitting immediately in front of the wheel-house, where an old Swedish boatswain whom we called 'Frithiof the Dane' was at the wheel, pretending that he could not hear our stories. Once or twice Frithiof spun the spokes curiously, and Keller lifted his head from a long chair to ask, 'What is it? Can't you get any steerage-way on her?'

'There is a feel in the water,' said Frithiof, 'that I cannot understand. I think that we run downhills or somethings. She steers bad this morning.'

Nobody seems to know the laws that govern the pulse of the big waters. Sometimes even a landsman can tell that the solid ocean is atilt, and that the ship is working herself up a long unseen slope; and sometimes the captain says, when neither full steam nor fair wind justifies the length of a day's run, that the ship is sagging downhill; but how these ups and downs come about has not yet been settled authoritatively.

'No, it is a following sea,' said Frithiof; 'and with a following sea you shall not get good steerage-way.'

The sea was as smooth as a duck-pond, except for a regular oily swell. As I looked over the side to see where it might be following us from, the sun rose in a perfectly clear sky and struck the water with its light so sharply that it seemed as though the sea should clang like a burnished gong. The wake of the screw and the little white streak cut by the log-line hanging over the stern were the only marks on the water as far as eye could reach.

Keller rolled out of his chair and went aft to get a pine-apple from the ripening stock that was hung inside the after awning.

'Frithiof, the log-line has got tired of swimming. It's coming home,' he drawled.

'What?' said Frithiof, his voice jumping several octaves.

'Coming home,' Keller repeated, leaning over the stern. I ran to his side and saw the log-line, which till then had been drawn tense over the stern railing, slacken, loop, and come up off the port quarter. Frithiof called up the speaking tube to the bridge, and the bridge answered, 'Yes, nine knots.' Then Frithiof spoke again, and the answer was, 'What do you want of the skipper?' and Frithiof bellowed, 'Call him up.'

By this time Zuyland, Keller, and myself had caught something of Frithiof's excitement, for any emotion on shipboard is most contagious. The captain ran out of his cabin, spoke to Frithiof, looked at the log-line, jumped on the bridge, and in a minute we felt the steamer swing round as Frithiof turned her.

''Going back to Cape Town?' said Keller.

Frithiof did not answer, but tore away at the wheel. Then he beckoned us three to help, and we held the wheel down till the *Rathmines* answered it, and we found ourselves looking into the white of our own wake, with the still oily sea tearing past our bows, though we were not going more than half steam ahead.

The captain stretched out his arm from the bridge and shouted. A minute later I would have given a great deal to have shouted too, for one-half of the sea seemed to shoulder itself above the other half, and came on in the shape of a hill. There was neither crest, comb, nor curl-over to it; nothing but black water with little waves chasing each other about the flanks. I saw it stream past and on a level with the *Rathmines'* bow-plates before the steamer hove up her bulk to rise, and I argued that this would be the last of all earthly voyages for me. Then we lifted for ever and ever and ever, till I heard Keller saying in my ear, 'The bowels of the deep, good Lord!' and the *Rathmines* stood poised, her screw-racing and drumming on the slope of a hollow that stretched downwards for a good half-mile.

We went down that hollow, nose under for the most part, and the air smelt wet and muddy, like that of an emptied aquarium. There was a second hill to climb; I saw that much: but the water came aboard and carried me aft till it jammed me against the wheel-house door, and before I could catch breath or clear my eyes again we were rolling to and fro in torn water, with the scuppers pouring like eaves in a thunderstorm.

'There were three waves,' said Keller; 'and the stoke-hold's flooded.'

The firemen were on deck waiting, apparently, to be drowned. The engineer came and dragged them below, and the crew, gasping, began to work the clumsy Board of Trade pump. That showed nothing serious, and when I understood that the *Rathmines* was really on the water, and not beneath it, I asked what had happened.

'The captain says it was a blow-up under the sea—a volcano,' said Keller.

'It hasn't warmed anything,' I said. I was feeling bitterly cold, and cold was almost unknown in those waters.

I went below to change my clothes, and when I came up everything was wiped out in clinging white fog.

'Are there going to be any more surprises?' said Keller to the captain.

'I don't know. Be thankful you are alive, gentlemen. That's a tidal wave thrown up by a volcano. Probably the bottom of the sea has been lifted a few feet somewhere or other. I can't quite understand this cold spell. Our sea-thermometer says the surface water is 44°, and it should be 68° at least.'

'It's abominable,' said Keller, shivering. 'But hadn't you better attend to the fog-horn? It seems to me that I heard something.'

'Heard! Good heavens!' said the captain from the bridge, 'I should think you did.' He pulled the string of our fog-horn, which was a weak one. It sputtered and choked, because the stoke-hold was full of water and the fires were half drowned, and at last gave out a moan. It was answered from the fog by one of the most appalling steam sirens I have ever heard. Keller turned as white as I did, for the fog, the cold fog, was upon us, and any man may be forgiven for fearing a death he cannot see.

'Give her steam there!' said the captain to the engine-room. 'Steam for the whistle, if we have to go dead slow.'

We bellowed again, and the damp dripped off the awnings on to the deck as we listened for the reply. It seemed to be astern this time, but much nearer than before.

'The *Pembroke Castle* on us!' said Keller; and then, viciously, 'Well, thank God, we shall sink her too.'

'It's a side-wheel steamer,' I whispered. 'Can't you hear the paddles?'

This time we whistled and roared till the steam gave out, and the answer nearly deafened us. There was a sound of frantic threshing in the water, apparently about fifty yards away, and something shot past in the whiteness that looked as though it were gray and red.

'The *Pembroke Castle* bottom up,' said Keller, who, being a journalist, always sought for explanations. 'That's the colours of a Castle liner. We're in for a big thing.'

'The sea is bewitched,' said Frithiof from the wheel-house. 'There are *two* steamers!'

Another siren sounded on our bow, and the little steamer rolled in the wash of something that had passed unseen.

'We're evidently in the middle of a fleet,' said Keller quietly. 'If one doesn't run us down, the other will. Phew! What in creation is that?'

I sniffed, for there was a poisonous rank smell in the cold air—a smell that I had smelt before.

'If I was on land I should say that it was an alligator. It smells like musk,' I answered.

'Not ten thousand alligators could make that smell,' said Zuyland; 'I have smelt them.'

'Bewitched! Bewitched!' said Frithiof. 'The sea she is turned upside down, and we are walking along the bottom.'

Again the *Rathmines* rolled in the wash of some unseen ship, and a silver-gray wave broke over the bow, leaving on the deck a sheet of sediment—the gray broth that has its place in the fathomless deeps of the sea. A sprinkling of the wave fell on my face, and it was so cold that it stung as boiling water stings. The dead and most untouched deep water of the sea had been heaved to the top by the submarine volcano—the chill still water that kills all life and smells of desolation and emptiness. We did not need either the blinding fog or that indescribable smell of musk to make us unhappy—we were shivering with cold and wretchedness where we stood.

'The hot air on the cold water makes this fog,' said the captain; 'it ought to clear in a little time.'

'Whistle, oh! whistle, and let's get out of it,' said Keller

The captain whistled again, and far and far astern the invisible twin steam-sirens answered us. Their blasting shriek grew louder, till at last it seemed to tear out of the fog just above our quarter, and I cowered while the *Rathmines* plunged bows under on a double swell that crossed.

'No more,' said Frithiof, 'it is not good any more. Let us get away, in the name of God.'

'Now if a torpedo-boat with a *City of Paris* siren went mad and broke her moorings and hired a friend to help her, it's just conceivable that we might be carried as we are now. Otherwise this thing is——'

The last words died on Keller's lips, his eyes began to start from his head, and his jaw fell. Some six or seven feet above the port bulwarks, framed in fog, and as utterly unsupported as the full moon, hung a Face. It was not human, and it certainly was not animal, for it did not belong to this earth as known to man. The mouth was open, revealing a ridiculously tiny tongue—as absurd as the tongue of an elephant; there were tense wrinkles of white skin at the angles of the drawn lips, white feelers like those of a barbel sprung from the lower jaw, and there was no sign of teeth within the mouth. But the horror of the face lay in the eyes, for those were sightless—white, in sockets as white as scraped bone, and blind. Yet for all this the face, wrinkled as the mask of a lion is drawn in Assyrian sculpture, was alive with rage and terror. One long white feeler touched our bulwarks. Then the face disappeared with the swiftness of a blindworm popping into its burrow, and the next thing that I remember is my own voice in my own ears, saying gravely to the mainmast, 'But the air-bladder ought to have been forced out of its mouth, you know.'

Keller came up to me, ashy white. He put his hand into his pocket, took a cigar, bit it, dropped it, thrust his shaking thumb into his mouth and mumbled, 'The giant gooseberry and the raining frogs! Gimme a light—gimme a light! Say, gimme a light.' A little bead of blood dropped from his thumb-joint.

I respected the motive, though the manifestation was absurd. 'Stop, you'll bite your thumb off,' I said, and Keller laughed brokenly as he picked up his cigar. Only Zuyland, leaning over the port bulwarks, seemed self-possessed. He declared later that he was very sick.

'We've seen it,' he said, turning round. 'That is it.'

'What?' said Keller, chewing the unlighted cigar.

As he spoke the fog was blown into shreds, and we saw the sea, gray with mud, rolling on every side of us and empty of all life. Then in one spot it bubbled and became like the pot of ointment that the Bible speaks of. From that wide-ringed trouble the Thing came up—a gray and red Thing with a neck—a Thing that bellowed and writhed in pain. Frithiof drew in his breath and held it till the red letters of the ship's name, woven across his jersey, straggled and opened out as though they had been type badly set. Then he said with a little cluck in his throat, 'Ah me! It is blind. *Hur illa*! That thing is blind,' and a murmur of pity went through us all, for we could see that the thing on the water was blind and in pain. Something had gashed and cut the great sides cruelly and the blood was spurting out. The gray ooze of the undermost sea lay in the monstrous wrinkles of the back, and poured away in sluices The blind white head flung back and battered the wounds, and the body in its torment rose clear of the red and gray waves till we saw a pair of quivering shoulders streaked with weed and rough with shells, but as white in the clear spaces as the hairless, maneless, blind, toothless head. Afterwards, came a dot on the horizon and the sound of a shrill scream, and it was as though a shuttle shot all across the sea in one breath, and a second head and neck tore through the levels, driving a whispering wall of water to right and left. The two Things met—the one untouched and the other in its death-throe—male and female, we said, the female coming to the male. She circled round him bellowing, and laid her neck across the curve of his great turtle-back, and he disappeared under water for an instant, but flung up again, grunting in agony while the blood ran. Once the entire head and neck shot clear of the water and stiffened, and I heard Keller saying, as though he was watching a street accident, 'Give him air. For God's sake, give him air.' Then the death-struggle began, with crampings and twistings and jerkings of the white bulk to and fro, till our little steamer rolled again, and each gray wave coated her plates with the gray slime. The sun was clear, there was no wind, and we watched, the whole crew, stokers and all, in wonder and pity, but chiefly pity. The Thing was so helpless, and, save for his mate, so alone. No human eye should have beheld him; it was monstrous and indecent to exhibit him there in trade waters between atlas degrees of latitude. He had been spewed up, mangled and dying, from his rest on the sea-floor, where he might have lived till the Judgment Day, and we saw the tides of his life go from him as an angry tide goes out across rocks in the teeth of a landward gale. His mate lay rocking on the water a little distance off, bellowing continually, and the smell of musk came down upon the ship making us cough.

At last the battle for life ended in a batter of coloured seas. We saw the writhing neck fall like a flail, the carcase turn sideways, showing the glint of a white belly and the inset of a gigantic hind leg or flipper. Then all sank, and sea boiled over it, while the mate swam round and round, darting her head in every direction. Though we might have feared that she would attack the steamer, no power on earth could have drawn any one of us from our places that hour. We watched, holding our breaths. The mate paused in her search; we could hear the wash beating along her sides; reared her neck as high as she could reach, blind and lonely in all that loneliness of the sea, and sent one desperate bellow booming across the swells as an oyster-shell skips across a pond. Then she made off to the westward, the sun shining on the white head and the wake behind it, till nothing was left to see but a little pin point of silver on the horizon. We stood on our course again; and the *Rathmines*, coated with the sea-sediment from bow to stern, looked like a ship made gray with terror.

. . . .

'We must pool our notes,' was the first coherent remark from Keller. 'We're three trained journalists—we hold absolutely the biggest scoop on record. Start fair.'

I objected to this. Nothing is gained by collaboration in journalism when all deal with the same facts, so we went to work each according to his own lights. Keller triple-headed his account, talked about our 'gallant captain,' and wound up with an allusion to American enterprise in that it was a citizen of Dayton, Ohio, that had seen the sea-serpent. This sort of thing would have discredited the Creation, much more a mere sea tale, but as a specimen of the picture-writing of a half-civilised people it was very interesting. Zuyland took a heavy column and a half, giving approximate lengths and breadths, and the whole list of the crew whom he had sworn on oath to testify to his facts. There was nothing fantastic or flamboyant in Zuyland. I wrote three-quarters of a leaded bourgeois column, roughly speaking, and refrained from putting any journalese into it for reasons that had begun to appear to me.

Keller was insolent with joy. He was going to cable from Southampton to the New York *World*, mail his account to America on the same day, paralyse London with his three columns of loosely knitted headlines, and generally efface the earth. 'You'll see how I work a big scoop when I get it,' he said.

'Is this your first visit to England?' I asked.

'Yes,' said he. 'You don't seem to appreciate the beauty of our scoop. It's pyramidal—the death of the sea-serpent! Good heavens alive, man, it's the biggest thing ever vouchsafed to a paper!'

'Curious to think that it will never appear in any paper, isn't it?' I said.

Zuyland was near me, and he nodded quickly.

'What do you mean?' said Keller. 'If you're enough of a Britisher to throw this thing away, I shan't. I thought you were a newspaper-man.'

'I am. That's why I know. Don't be an ass, Keller. Remember, I'm seven hundred years your senior, and what your grandchildren may learn five hundred years hence, I learned from my grandfathers about five hundred years ago. You won't do it, because you can't.'

This conversation was held in open sea, where everything seems possible, some hundred miles from Southampton. We passed the Needles Light at dawn, and the lifting day showed the stucco villas on the green and the awful orderliness of England—line upon line, wall upon wall, solid stone dock and monolithic pier. We waited an hour in the Customs shed, and there was ample time for the effect to soak in.

'Now, Keller, you face the music. The *Havel* goes out to-day. Mail by her, and I'll take you to the telegraph-office,' I said.

I heard Keller gasp as the influence of the land closed about him, cowing him as they say Newmarket Heath cows a young horse unused to open courses.

'I want to retouch my stuff. Suppose we wait till we get to London?' he said.

Zuyland, by the way, had torn up his account and

thrown it overboard that morning early. His reasons were my reasons.

In the train Keller began to revise his copy, and every time that he looked at the trim little fields, the red villas, and the embankments of the line, the blue pencil plunged remorselessly through the slips. He appeared to have dredged the dictionary for adjectives. I could think of none that he had not used. Yet he was a perfectly sound poker-player and never showed more cards than were sufficient to take the pool.

'Aren't you going to leave him a single bellow?' I asked sympathetically. 'Remember, everything goes in the States, from a trouser-button to a double-eagle.'

'That's just the curse of it,' said Keller below his breath. 'We've played 'em for suckers so often that when it comes to the golden truth—I'd like to try this on a London paper. You have first call there, though.'

'Not in the least. I'm not touching the thing in our papers. I shall be happy to leave 'em all to you; but surely you'll cable it home?'

'No. Not if I can make the scoop here and see the Britishers sit up.'

'You won't do it with three columns of slushy headline, believe me. They don't sit up as quickly as some people.'

'I'm beginning to think that too. Does *nothing* make any difference in this country?' he said, looking out of the window. 'How old is that farmhouse?'

'New. It can't be more than two hundred years at the most.'

'Um. Fields, too?"

'That hedge there must have been clipped for about eighty years.'

'Labour cheap—eh?'

'Pretty much. Well, I suppose you'd like to try the *Times*, wouldn't you?'

'No,' said Keller, looking at Winchester Cathedral. ''Might as well try to electrify a haystack. And to think that the *World* would take three columns and ask for more —with illustrations too! It's sickening.'

'But the *Times* might,' I began.

Keller flung his paper across the carriage, and it opened in its austere majesty of solid type—opened with the crackle of an encyclopædia.

'Might! You *might* work your way through the bow-plates of a cruiser. Look at that first page!'

'It strikes you that way, does it?' I said. 'Then I'd recommend you to try a light and frivolous journal.'

'With a thing like this of mine—of ours? It's sacred history!'

I showed him a paper which I conceived would be after his own heart, in that it was modelled on American lines.

'That's homey,' he said, 'but it's not the real thing. Now, I should like one of these fat old *Times* columns. Probably there'd be a bishop in the office, though.'

When we reached London Keller disappeared in the direction of the Strand. What his experiences may have been I cannot tell, but it seems that he invaded the office of an evening paper at 11.45 a.m. (I told him English editors were most idle at that hour), and mentioned my name as that of a witness to the truth of his story.

'I was nearly fired out,' he said furiously at lunch. 'As soon as I mentioned you, the old man said that I was to tell you that they didn't want any more of your practical jokes, and that you knew the hours to call if you had anything to sell, and that they'd see you condemned before they helped to puff one of your infernal yarns in advance. Say, what record do you hold for truth in this country, anyway?'

'A beauty. You ran up against it, that's all. Why

don't you leave the English papers alone and cable to New York? Everything goes over there.'

'Can't you see that's just why?' he repeated.

'I saw it a long time ago. You don't intend to cable then?'

'Yes, I do,' he answered, in the over-emphatic voice of one who does not know his own mind.

That afternoon I walked him abroad and about, over the streets that run between the pavements like channels of grooved and tongued lava, over the bridges that are made of enduring stone, through subways floored and sided with yard-thick concrete, between houses that are never rebuilt, and by river steps hewn, to the eye, from the living rock. A black fog chased us into Westminster Abbey, and, standing there in the darkness, I could hear the wings of the dead centuries circling round the head of Litchfield A. Keller, journalist, of Dayton, Ohio, U.S.A., whose mission it was to make the Britishers sit up.

He stumbled gasping into the thick gloom, and the roar of the traffic came to his bewildered ears.

'Let's go to the telegraph-office and cable,' I said. 'Can't you hear the New York *World* crying for news of the great sea-serpent, blind, white, and smelling of musk, stricken to death by a submarine volcano, and assisted by his loving wife to die in mid-ocean, as visualised by an American citizen, the breezy, newsy, brainy newspaper man of Dayton, Ohio? 'Rah for the Buckeye State. Step lively! Both gates! Szz! Boom! Aah!' Keller was a Princeton man, and he seemed to need encouragement.

'You've got me on your own ground,' said he, tugging at his overcoat pocket. He pulled out his copy, with the cable forms—for he had written out his telegram—and put them all into my hand, groaning, 'I pass. If I hadn't come to your cursed country—If I'd sent it off at Southampton—If I ever get you west of the Alleghannies, if———'

'Never mind, Keller. It isn't your fault. It's the fault of your country. If you had been seven hundred years older you'd have done what I am going to do.'

'What are you going to do?'

'Tell it as a lie.'

'Fiction?' This with the full-blooded disgust of a journalist for the illegitimate branch of the profession.

'You can call it that if you like. I shall call it a lie.'

And a lie it has become; for Truth is a naked lady, and if by accident she is drawn up from the bottom of the sea, it behoves a gentleman either to give her a print petticoat or to turn his face to the wall and vow that he did not see.

MOWGLI'S BROTHERS

Now Chil the Kite brings home the night
    That Mang the Bat sets free—
The herds are shut in byre and hut
    For loosed till dawn are we.
This is the hour of pride and power,
    Talon and tush and claw.
Oh hear the call !—Good hunting all
    That keep the Jungle Law !

Night-Song in the Jungle.

It was seven o'clock of a very warm evening in the Seeonee hills when Father Wolf woke up from his day's rest, scratched himself, yawned, and spread out his paws one after the other to get rid of the sleepy feeling in their tips. Mother Wolf lay with her big gray nose dropped across her four tumbling, squealing cubs, and the moon shone into the mouth of the cave where they all lived. 'Augrh !' said Father Wolf, 'it is time to hunt again'; and he was going to spring down hill when a little shadow with a bushy tail crossed the threshold and whined : 'Good luck go with you, O Chief of the Wolves ; and good luck and strong white teeth go with the noble children, that they may never forget the hungry in this world.'

It was the jackal—Tabaqui, the Dish-licker—and the wolves of India despise Tabaqui because he runs about making mischief, and telling tales, and eating rags and pieces of leather from the village rubbish-heaps. But they are afraid of him too, because Tabaqui, more than any one else in the jungle, is apt to go mad, and then he forgets that he was ever afraid of any one, and runs through the forest biting everything in his way. Even the tiger runs and hides when little Tabaqui goes mad, for madness is the most disgraceful thing that can overtake a wild creature. We call it hydrophobia, but they call it *dewanee*—the madness—and run.

'Enter, then, and look,' said Father Wolf, stiffly; 'but there is no food here.'

'For a wolf, no,' said Tabaqui; 'but for so mean a person as myself a dry bone is a good feast. Who are we, the Gidur-log [the jackal people], to pick and choose?' He scuttled to the back of the cave, where he found the bone of a buck with some meat on it, and sat cracking the end merrily.

'All thanks for this good meal,' he said, licking his lips. 'How beautiful are the noble children! How large are their eyes! And so young too! Indeed, indeed, I might have remembered that the children of kings are men from the beginning.'

Now, Tabaqui knew as well as any one else that there is nothing so unlucky as to compliment children to their faces; and it pleased him to see Mother and Father Wolf look uncomfortable.

Tabaqui sat still, rejoicing in the mischief that he had made, and then he said spitefully:

'Shere Khan, the Big One, has shifted his hunting-grounds. He will hunt among these hills for the next moon, so he has told me.'

Shere Khan was the tiger who lived near the Waingunga River, twenty miles away.

'He has no right!' Father Wolf began angrily—'By the Law of the Jungle he has no right to change his quarters without due warning. He will frighten every head of game within ten miles, and I—I have to kill for two, these days.'

'His mother did not call him Lungri [the Lame One] for nothing,' said Mother Wolf, quietly. He has been lame in one foot from his birth. That is why he has only killed cattle. Now the villagers of the Waingunga are angry with him, and he has come here to make *our* villagers angry. They will scour the jungle for him when he is far away, and we and our children must run when the grass is set alight. Indeed, we are very grateful to Shere Khan!'

'Shall I tell him of your gratitude?' said Tabaqui.

'Out!' snapped Father Wolf. 'Out and hunt with thy master. Thou hast done harm enough for one night.'

'I go,' said Tabaqui, quietly. 'Ye can hear Shere Khan below in the thickets. I might have saved myself the message.'

Father Wolf listened, and below in the valley that ran down to a little river, he heard the dry, angry, snarly, singsong whine of a tiger who has caught nothing and does not care if all the jungle knows it.

'The fool!' said Father Wolf. 'To begin a night's work with that noise. Does he think that our buck are like his fat Waingunga bullocks?'

'H'sh. It is neither bullock nor buck he hunts to-night,' said Mother Wolf. 'It is Man.' The whine had changed to a sort of humming purr that seemed to come from every quarter of the compass. It was the noise that bewilders woodcutters and gipsies sleeping in the open, and makes them run sometimes into the very mouth of the tiger.

'Man!' said Father Wolf, showing all his white teeth. 'Faugh! Are there not enough beetles and frogs in the tanks that he must eat Man, and on our ground too!'

The Law of the Jungle, which never orders anything without a reason, forbids every beast to eat Man except when he is killing to show his children how to kill, and then he must hunt outside the hunting-grounds of his pack or tribe. The real reason for this is that man-killing means, sooner or later, the arrival of white men on elephants, with guns, and hundreds of brown men with gongs and rockets and torches. Then everybody in the jungle suffers. The reason the beasts give among themselves is that Man is the weakest and most defenceless of all living things, and it is unsportsmanlike to touch him. They say too—and it is true—that man-eaters become mangy, and lose their teeth.

The purr grew louder, and ended in the full-throated 'Aaarh!' of the tiger's charge.

Then there was a howl—an untigerish howl—from Shere Khan. 'He has missed,' said Mother Wolf. 'What is it?'

Father Wolf ran out a few paces and heard Shere Khan muttering and mumbling savagely, as he tumbled about in the scrub.

'The fool has had no more sense than to jump at a wood-cutters' camp-fire, and has burned his feet,' said Father Wolf, with a grunt. 'Tabaqui is with him.'

'Something is coming up hill,' said Mother Wolf, twitching one ear. 'Get ready.'

The bushes rustled a little in the thicket, and Father Wolf dropped with his haunches under him, ready for his leap. Then, if you had been watching, you would have seen the most wonderful thing in the world—the wolf checked in mid-spring. He made his bound before he saw what it was he was jumping at, and then he tried to stop himself. The result was that he shot up straight into the air for four or five feet, landing almost where he left ground.

'Man!' he snapped. 'A man's cub. Look!'

Directly in front of him, holding on by a low branch, stood a naked brown baby who could just walk—as soft and as dimpled a little atom as ever came to a wolf's cave at night. He looked up into Father Wolf's face, and laughed.

'Is that a man's cub?' said Mother Wolf. 'I have never seen one. Bring it here.'

A wolf accustomed to moving his own cubs can, if necessary, mouth an egg without breaking it, and though Father Wolf's jaws closed right on the child's back not a tooth even scratched the skin, as he laid it down among the cubs.

'How little! How naked, and—how bold!' said Mother Wolf, softly. The baby was pushing his way between the cubs to get close to the warm hide. 'Ahai! He is taking his meal with the others. And so this is a man's cub. Now, was there ever a wolf that could boast of a man's cub among her children?'

'I have heard now and again of such a thing, but never in our Pack or in my time,' said Father Wolf. 'He is altogether without hair, and I could kill him with a touch of my foot. But see, he looks up and is not afraid.'

The moonlight was blocked out of the mouth of the cave, for Shere Khan's great square head and shoulders were thrust into the entrance. Tabaqui, behind him, was squeaking: 'My lord, my lord, it went in here!'

'Shere Khan does us great honour,' said Father Wolf, but his eyes were very angry. 'What does Shere Khan need?'

'My quarry. A man's cub went this way,' said Shere Khan. 'Its parents have run off. Give it to me.'

Shere Khan had jumped at a woodcutters' camp-fire, as Father Wolf had said, and was furious from the pain of his burned feet. But Father Wolf knew that the mouth of the cave was too narrow for a tiger to come in by. Even where he was, Shere Khan's shoulders and fore paws were cramped for want of room, as a man's would be if he tried to fight in a barrel.

'The Wolves are a free people,' said Father Wolf. 'They take orders from the Head of the Pack, and not from any striped cattle-dealer. The man's cub is ours—to kill if we choose.'

'Ye choose and ye do not choose! What talk is this of choosing? By the bull that I killed, am I to stand nosing into your dog's den for my fair dues? It is I, Shere Khan, who speak!'

The tiger's roar filled the cave with thunder. Mother Wolf shook herself clear of the cubs and sprang forward, her eyes, like two green moons in the darkness, facing the blazing eyes of Shere Khan.

'And it is I, Raksha [The Demon], who answer. The man's cub is mine, Lungri—mine to me! He shall not be killed. He shall live to run with the Pack and to hunt with the Pack; and in the end, look you, hunter of little naked cubs—frog-eater—fish-killer—he shall hunt *thee*! Now get hence, or by the Sambhur that I killed (*I* eat no starved cattle), back thou goest to thy mother, burned beast of the jungle, lamer than ever thou camest into the world! Go!'

Father Wolf looked on amazed. He had almost forgotten the days when he had won Mother Wolf in fair fight from five other wolves, when she ran in the Pack and was not called The Demon for compliment's sake. Shere Khan might have faced Father Wolf, but he could not stand up against Mother Wolf, for he knew that where he was she had all the advantage of the ground, and would fight to the death. So he backed out of the cave-mouth growling, and when he was clear he shouted:—

'Each dog barks in his own yard! We will see what the Pack will say to this fostering of man-cubs. The cub is mine, and to my teeth he will come in the end, O bush-tailed thieves!'

Mother Wolf threw herself down panting among the cubs, and Father Wolf said to her gravely:—

'Shere Khan speaks this much truth. The cub must

be shown to the Pack. Wilt thou still keep him, Mother?'

'Keep him!' she gasped. 'He came naked, by night, alone and very hungry; yet he was not afraid! Look, he has pushed one of my babes to one side already. And that lame butcher would have killed him and would have run off to the Waingunga while the villagers here hunted through all our lairs in revenge! Keep him? Assuredly I will keep him. Lie still, little frog. O thou Mowgli—for Mowgli the Frog I will call thee—the time will come when thou wilt hunt Shere Khan as he has hunted thee.'

'But what will our Pack say?' said Father Wolf.

The Law of the Jungle lays down very clearly that any wolf may, when he marries, withdraw from the Pack he belongs to; but as soon as his cubs are old enough to stand on their feet he must bring them to the Pack Council, which is generally held once a month at full moon, in order that the other wolves may identify them. After that inspection the cubs are free to run where they please, and until they have killed their first buck no excuse is accepted if a grown wolf of the Pack kills one of them. The punishment is death where the murderer can be found; and if you think for a minute you will see that this must be so.

Father Wolf waited till his cubs could run a little, and then on the night of the Pack Meeting took them and Mowgli and Mother Wolf to the Council Rock—a hilltop covered with stones and boulders where a hundred wolves could hide. Akela, the great gray Lone Wolf, who led all the Pack by strength and cunning, lay out at full length on his rock, and below him sat forty or more wolves of every size and colour, from badger-coloured veterans who could handle a buck alone, to young black three-year-olds who thought they could. The Lone Wolf had led them for a year now. He had fallen twice into a wolf-trap in his youth, and once he had been beaten and left for dead; so he knew the manners and customs of men. There was very little talking at the rock. The cubs tumbled over each other in the centre of the circle where their mothers and fathers sat, and now and again a senior wolf would go quietly up to a cub, look at him carefully, and return to his place on noiseless feet. Sometimes a mother would push her cub far out into the moonlight, to be sure that he had not been overlooked. Akela from his rock would cry: 'Ye know the Law—ye know the Law. Look well, O Wolves!' and the anxious mothers would take up the call: 'Look—look well, O Wolves!'

At last—and Mother Wolf's neck-bristles lifted as the time came—Father Wolf pushed 'Mowgli the Frog,' as they called him, into the centre, where he sat laughing and playing with some pebbles that glistened in the moonlight.

Akela never raised his head from his paws, but went on with the monotonous cry: 'Look well!' A muffled roar came up from behind the rocks—the voice of Shere Khan crying: 'The cub is mine. Give him to me. What have the Free People to do with a man's cub?' Akela never even twitched his ears: all he said was: 'Look well, O Wolves! What have the Free People to do with the orders of any save the Free People? Look well!'

There was a chorus of deep growls, and a young wolf in his fourth year flung back Shere Khan's question to Akela: 'What have the Free People to do with a man's cub?' Now the Law of the Jungle lays down that if there is any dispute as to the right of a cub to be accepted by the Pack, he must be spoken for by at least two members of the Pack who are not his father and mother.

'Who speaks for this cub?' said Akela. 'Among the Free People who speaks?' There was no answer, and Mother Wolf got ready for what she knew would be her last fight, if things came to fighting.

Then the only other creature who is allowed at the Pack

Council—Baloo, the sleepy brown bear who teaches the wolf cubs the Law of the Jungle: old Baloo, who can come and go where he pleases because he eats only nuts and roots and honey—rose up on his hind quarters and grunted.

'The man's cub—the man's cub?' he said. '*I* speak for the man's cub. There is no harm in a man's cub. I have no gift of words, but I speak the truth. Let him run with the Pack, and be entered with the others. I myself will teach him.'

'We need yet another,' said Akela. 'Baloo has spoken, and he is our teacher for the young cubs. Who speaks beside Baloo?'

A black shadow dropped down into the circle. It was Bagheera the Black Panther, inky black all over, but with the panther markings showing up in certain lights like the pattern of watered silk. Everybody knew Bagheera, and nobody cared to cross his path; for he was as cunning as Tabaqui, as bold as the wild buffalo, and as reckless as the wounded elephant. But he had a voice as soft as wild honey dripping from a tree, and a skin softer than down.

'O Akela, and ye the Free People,' he purred, 'I have no right in your assembly; but the Law of the Jungle says that if there is a doubt which is not a killing matter in regard to a new cub, the life of that cub may be bought at a price. And the Law does not say who may or may not pay that price. Am I right?'

'Good! good!' said the young wolves, who are always hungry. 'Listen to Bagheera. The cub can be bought for a price. It is the Law.'

'Knowing that I have no right to speak here, I ask your leave.'

'Speak then,' cried twenty voices.

'To kill a naked cub is shame. Besides, he may make better sport for you when he is grown. Baloo has spoken in his behalf. Now to Baloo's word I will add one bull, and a fat one, newly killed, not half a mile from here, if ye will accept the man's cub according to the Law. Is it difficult?'

There was a clamour of scores of voices, saying: 'What matter? He will die in the winter rains. He will scorch in the sun. What harm can a naked frog do us? Let him run with the Pack. Where is the bull, Bagheera? Let him be accepted.' And then came Akela's deep bay, crying: Look well—look well, O Wolves!'

Mowgli was still deeply interested in the pebbles, and he did not notice when the wolves came and looked at him one by one. At last they all went down the hill for the dead bull, and only Akela, Bagheera, Baloo, and Mowgli's own wolves were left. Shere Khan roared still in the night, for he was very angry that Mowgli had not been handed over to him.

'Ay, roar well,' said Bagheera, under his whiskers; 'for the time comes when this naked thing will make thee roar to another tune, or I know nothing of man.'

'It was well done,' said Akela. 'Men and their cubs are very wise. He may be a help in time.'

'Truly, a help in time of need; for none can hope to lead the Pack for ever,' said Bagheera.

Akela said nothing He was thinking of the time that comes to every leader of every pack when his strength goes from him and he gets feebler and feebler, till at last he is killed by the wolves and a new leader comes up—to be killed in his turn.

'Take him away,' he said to Father Wolf, 'and train him as befits one of the Free People.'

And that is how Mowgli was entered into the Seeonee wolf-pack for the price of a bull and on Baloo's good word.

* * * * *

Now you must be content to skip ten or eleven whole years, and only guess at all the wonderful life Mowgli led among the wolves, because if it were written out it would fill ever so many books. He grew up with the cubs, though they, of course, were grown wolves almost before he was a child, and Father Wolf taught him his business, and the meaning of things in the jungle, till every rustle in the grass, every breath of the warm night air, every note of the owls above his head, every scratch of a bat's claws as it roosted for a while in a tree, and every splash of every little fish jumping in a pool, meant just as much to him as the work of his office means to a business man. When he was not learning he sat out in the sun and slept, and ate and went to sleep again; when he felt dirty or hot he swam in the forest pools; and when he wanted honey (Baloo told him that honey and nuts were just as pleasant to eat as raw meat) he climbed up for it, and that Bagheera showed him how to do. Bagheera would lie out on a branch and call, 'Come along, Little Brother,' and at first Mowgli would cling like the sloth, but afterward he would fling himself through the branches almost as boldly as the gray ape. He took his place at the Council Rock, too, when the Pack met, and there he discovered that if he stared hard at any wolf, the wolf would be forced to drop his eyes, and so he used to stare for fun. At other times he would pick the long thorns out of the pads of his friends, for wolves suffer terribly from thorns and burs in their coats. He would go down the hillside into the cultivated lands by night, and look very curiously at the villagers in their huts, but he had a mistrust of men because Bagheera showed him a square box with a drop-gate so cunningly hidden in the jungle that he nearly walked into it, and told him that it was a trap. He loved better than anything else to go with Bagheera into the dark warm heart of the forest, to sleep all through the drowsy day, and at night see how Bagheera did his killing. Bagheera killed right and left as he felt hungry, and so did Mowgli—with one exception. As soon as he was old enough to understand things, Bagheera told him that he must never touch cattle because he had been bought into the Pack at the price of a bull's life. 'All the jungle is thine,' said Bagheera, 'and thou canst kill everything that thou art strong enough to kill; but for the sake of the bull that bought thee thou must never kill or eat any cattle young or old. That is the Law of the Jungle.' Mowgli obeyed faithfully.

And he grew and grew strong as a boy must grow who does not know that he is learning any lessons, and who has nothing in the world to think of except things to eat.

Mother Wolf told him once or twice that Shere Khan was not a creature to be trusted, and that some day he must kill Shere Khan; but though a young wolf would have remembered that advice every hour, Mowgli forgot it because he was only a boy—though he would have called himself a wolf if he had been able to speak in any human tongue.

Shere Khan was always crossing his path in the jungle, for as Akela grew older and feebler tbe lame tiger had come to be great friends with the younger wolves of the Pack, who followed him for scraps, a thing Akela would never have allowed if he had dared to push his authority to the proper bounds. Then Shere Khan would flatter them and wonder that such fine young hunters were content to be led by a dying wolf and a man's cub 'They tell me,' Shere Khan would say, 'that at Council ye dare not look him between the eyes'; and the young wolves would growl and bristle.

Bagheera, who had eyes and ears everywhere, knew something of this, and once or twice he told Mowgli in so many words that Shere Khan would kill him some day; and Mowgli would laugh and answer: 'I have the Pack and I have thee; and Baloo, though he is so lazy, might strike a blow or two for my sake. Why should I be afraid?'

It was one very warm day that a new notion came to Bagheera—born of something that he had heard. Perhaps Sahi the Porcupine had told him; but he said to Mowgli when they were deep in the jungle, as the boy lay with his head on Bagheera's beautiful black skin: 'Little Brother,' how often have I told thee that Shere Khan is thy enemy?'

'As many times as there are nuts on that palm,' said Mowgli, who, naturally, could not count. 'What of it? I am sleepy, Bagheera, and Shere Khan is all long tail and loud talk—like Mor the Peacock.'

'But this is no time for sleeping. Baloo knows it; I know it; the Pack know it; and even the foolish, foolish deer know. Tabaqui has told thee, too.'

'Ho! ho!' said Mowgli. 'Tabaqui came to me not long ago with some rude talk that I was a naked man's cub and not fit to dig pig-nuts; but I caught Tabaqui by the tail and swung him twice against a palm-tree to teach him better manners.'

'That was foolishness; for though Tabaqui is a mischief-maker, he would have told thee of something that concerned thee closely. Open those eyes, Little Brother. Shere Khan dare not kill thee in the jungle; but remember, Akela is very old, and soon the day comes when he cannot kill his buck, and then he will be leader no more. Many of the wolves that looked thee over when thou wast brought to the Council first are old too, and the young wolves believe, as Shere Khan has taught them, that a man-cub has no place with the Pack. In a little time thou wilt be a man.'

'And what is a man that he should not run with his brothers?' said Mowgli. 'I was born in the jungle. I have obeyed the Law of the Jungle, and there is no wolf of ours from whose paws I have not pulled a thorn. Surely they are my brothers!'

Bagheera stretched himself at full length and half shut his eyes. 'Little Brother,' said he, 'feel under my jaw.'

Mowgli put up his strong brown hand, and just under Bagheera's silky chin, where the giant rolling muscles were all hid by the glossy hair, he came upon a little bald spot.

'There is no one in the jungle that knows that I, Bagheera, carry that mark—the mark of the collar; and yet, Little Brother, I was born among men, and it was among men that my mother died—in the cages of the King's Palace at Oodeypore. It was because of this that I paid the price for thee at the Council when thou wast a little naked cub. Yes, I too was born among men. I had never seen the jungle. They fed me behind bars from an iron pan till one night I felt that I was Bagheera—the Panther—and no man's plaything, and I broke the silly lock with one blow of my paw and came away; and because I had learned the ways of men, I became more terrible in the jungle than Shere Khan. Is it not so?'

'Yes,' said Mowgli; 'all the jungle fear Bagheera—all except Mowgli.'

'Oh, *thou* art a man's cub,' said the Black Panther, very tenderly; 'and even as I returned to my jungle, so thou must go back to men at last,—to the men who are thy brothers,—if thou art not killed in the Council.'

'But why—but why should any wish to kill me?' said Mowgli.

'Look at me,' said Bagheera; and Mowgli looked at him steadily between the eyes. The big panther turned his head away in half a minute.

'*That* is why,' he said, shifting his paw on the leaves. 'Not even I can look thee between the eyes, and I was born among men, and I love thee, Little Brother. The others they hate thee because their eyes cannot meet thine; because thou art wise; because thou hast pulled out thorns from their feet—because thou art a man.'

'I did not know these things,' said Mowgli, sullenly; and he frowned under his heavy black eyebrows.

'What is the Law of the Jungle? Strike first and then give tongue. By thy very carelessness they know that thou art a man. But be wise. It is in my heart that when Akela misses his next kill,—and at each hunt it costs him more to pin the buck,—the Pack will turn against him and against thee. They will hold a jungle Council at the Rock, and then—and then—I have it!' said Bagheera, leaping up. 'Go thou down quickly to the men's huts in the valley, and take some of the Red Flower which they grow there, so that when the time comes thou mayest have even a stronger friend than I or Baloo or those of the Pack that love thee. Get the Red Flower.'

By Red Flower Bagheera meant fire, only no creature in the jungle will call fire by its proper name. Every beast lives in deadly fear of it, and invents a hundred ways of describing it.

'The Red Flower?' said Mowgli. 'That grows outside their huts in the twilight. I will get some.'

'There speaks the man's cub,' said Bagheera, proudly. 'Remember that it grows in little pots. Get one swiftly, and keep it by thee for time of need.'

'Good!' said Mowgli. 'I go. But art thou sure, O my Bagheera'—he slipped his arm round the splendid neck, and looked deep into the big eyes—'art thou sure that all this is Shere Khan's doing?'

'By the Broken Lock that freed me, I am sure, Little Brother.'

'Then, by the Bull that bought me, I will pay Shere Khan full tale for this, and it may be a little over,' said Mowgli; and he bounded away.

'That is a man. That is all a man,' said Bagheera to himself, lying down again. 'Oh, Shere Khan, never was a blacker hunting than that frog-hunt of thine ten years ago!'

Mowgli was far and far through the forest, running hard, and his heart was hot in him. He came to the cave as the evening mist rose, and drew breath, and looked down the valley. The cubs were out, but Mother Wolf, at the back of the cave, knew by his breathing that something was troubling her frog.

'What is it, Son?' she said.

'Some bat's chatter of Shere Khan,' he called back. 'I hunt among the ploughed fields to-night'; and he plunged downward through the bushes, to the stream at the bottom of the valley. There he checked, for he heard the yell of the Pack hunting, heard the bellow of a hunted Sambhur, and the snort as the buck turned at bay. Then there were wicked, bitter howls from the young wolves: 'Akela! Akela! Let the Lone Wolf show his strength. Room for the leader of the Pack! Spring, Akela!'

The Lone Wolf must have sprung and missed his hold, for Mowgli heard the snap of his teeth and then a yelp as the Sambhur knocked him over with his fore foot.

He did not wait for anything more, but dashed on; and the yells grew fainter behind him as he ran into the crop-lands where the villagers lived.

'Bagheera spoke truth,' he panted, as he nestled down in some cattle-fodder by the window of a hut. 'To-morrow is one day both for Akela and for me.'

Then he pressed his face close to the window and watched the fire on the hearth. He saw the husbandman's wife get up and feed it in the night with black lumps; and when the morning came and the mists were all white and cold, he saw the man's child pick up a wicker pot plastered inside with earth, fill it with lumps of red-hot charcoal, put it under his blanket, and go out to tend the cows in the byre.

'Is that all?' said Mowgli. 'If a cub can do it, there is nothing to fear'; so he strode round the corner and met the boy, took the pot from his hand, and disappeared into the mist while the boy howled with fear.

'They are very like me,' said Mowgli, blowing into the pot, as he had seen the woman do. 'This thing will die if I do not give it things to eat'; and he dropped twigs and dried bark on the red stuff. Half-way up the hill he met Bagheera with the morning dew shining like moonstones on his coat.

'Akela has missed,' said the Panther. 'They would have killed him last night, but they needed thee also. They were looking for thee on the hill.'

'I was among the ploughed lands. I am ready. See!' Mowgli held up the fire-pot.

'Good! Now I have seen men thrust a dry branch into that stuff, and presently the Red Flower blossomed at the end of it. Art thou not afraid?'

'No. Why should I fear? I remember now—if it is not a dream—how, before I was a Wolf, I lay beside the Red Flower, and it was warm and pleasant.'

All that day Mowgli sat in the cave tending his fire-pot and dipping dry branches into it to see how they looked. He found a branch that satisfied him, and in the evening when Tabaqui came to the cave and told him rudely enough that he was wanted at the Council Rock, he laughed till Tabaqui ran away. Then Mowgli went to the Council, still laughing.

Akela the lone wolf lay by the side of his rock as a sign that the leadership of the Pack was open, and Shere Khan with his following of scrap-fed wolves walked to and fro openly being flattered. Bagheera lay close to Mowgli, and the fire-pot was between Mowgli's knees. When they were all gathered together, Shere Khan began to speak—a thing he would never have dared to do when Akela was in his prime.

'He has no right,' whispered Bagheera. 'Say so. He is a dog's son. He will be frightened.'

Mowgli sprang to his feet. 'Free People,' he cried, 'does Shere Khan lead the Pack? What has a tiger to do with our leadership?'

'Seeing that the leadership is yet open, and being asked to speak—' Shere Khan began.

'By whom?' said Mowgli. 'Are we *all* jackals, to fawn on this cattle-butcher? The leadership of the Pack is with the Pack alone.'

There were yells of 'Silence, thou man's cub!' 'Let him speak. He has kept our Law'; and at last the seniors of the Pack thundered: 'Let the Dead Wolf speak.' When a leader of the Pack has missed his kill, he is called the Dead Wolf as long as he lives, which is not long

Akela raised his old head wearily:—

'Free People, and ye too, jackals of Shere Khan, for twelve seasons I have led ye to and from the kill, and in all that time not one has been trapped or maimed. Now I have missed my kill. Ye know how that plot was made. Ye know how ye brought me up to an untried buck to make my weakness known. It was cleverly done. Your right is to kill me here on the Council Rock, now. Therefore, I ask, who comes to make an end of the Lone Wolf? For it is my right, by the Law of the Jungle, that ye come one by one.'

There was a long hush, for no single wolf cared to fight Akela to the death. Then Shere Khan roared: 'Bah! what have we to do with this toothless fool? He is doomed to die! It is the man-cub who has lived too long. Free People, he was my meat from the first. Give him to me. I am weary of this man-wolf folly. He has troubled the jungle for ten seasons. Give me the man-cub, or I will hunt here always, and not give you one bone. He is a man, a man's child, and from the marrow of my bones I hate him!'

Then more than half the Pack yelled: 'A man! a man!

What has a man to do with us? Let him go to his own place.

'And turn all the people of the villages against us?' clamoured Shere Khan. 'No; give him to me. He is a man, and none of us can look him between the eyes.'

Akela lifted his head again, and said: 'He has eaten our food. He has slept with us. He has driven game for us. He has broken no word of the Law of the Jungle.'

'Also, I paid for him with a Bull when he was accepted. The worth of a bull is little, but Bagheera's honour is something that he will perhaps fight for,' said Bagheera, in his gentlest voice.

'A bull paid ten years ago!' the Pack snarled. 'What do we care for bones ten years old?'

'Or for a pledge?' said Bagheera, his white teeth bared under his lip. 'Well are ye called the Free People!'

'No man's cub can run with the people of the jungle,' howled Shere Khan. 'Give him to me!'

'He is our brother in all but blood,' Akela went on; 'and ye would kill him here! In truth, I have lived too long. Some of ye are eaters of cattle, and of others I have heard that, under Shere Khan's teaching, ye go by dark night and snatch children from the villager's door-step- Therefore I know ye to be cowards, and it is to cowards I speak. It is certain that I must die, and my life is of no worth, or I would offer that in the man-cub's place. But for the sake of the Honour of the Pack,—a little matter that by being without a leader ye have forgotten,—I promise that if ye let the man-cub go to his own place, I will not, when my time comes to die, bare one tooth against ye. I will die without fighting. That will at least save the Pack three lives. More I cannot do; but if ye will, I can save ye the shame that comes of killing a brother against whom there is no fault,—a brother spoken for and bought into the Pack according to the Law of the Jungle.'

'He is a man—a man—a man—!' snarled the Pack; and most of the wolves began to gather round Shere Khan, whose tail was beginning to switch.

'Now the business is in thy hands,' said Bagheera to Mowgli. '*We* can do no more except fight.'

Mowgli stood upright—the fire-pot in his hands. Then he stretched out his arms, and yawned in the face of the Council; but he was furious with rage and sorrow, for, wolf-like, the wolves had never told him how they hated him. 'Listen you!' he cried. 'There is no need for this dog's jabber. Ye have told me so often to-night that I am a man (and indeed I would have been a wolf with you to my life's end), that I feel your words are true. So I do not call ye my brothers any more, but *sag* [dogs], as a man should. What ye will do, and what ye will not do, is not yours to say. That matter is with *me*; and that we may see the matter more plainly, I, the man, have brought here a little of the Red Flower which ye, dogs, fear.'

He flung the fire-pot on the ground, and some of the red coals lit a tuft of dried moss that flared up, as all the Council drew back in terror before the leaping flames.

Mowgli thrust his dead branch into the fire till the twigs lit and crackled, and whirled it above his head among the cowering wolves.

'Thou art the master,' said Bagheera, in an undertone. 'Save Akela from the death. He was ever thy friend.'

Akela, the grim old wolf who had never asked for mercy in his life, gave one piteous look at Mowgli as the boy stood all naked, his long black hair tossing over his shoulders in the light of the blazing branch that made the shadows jump and quiver.

'Good!' said Mowgli, staring round slowly. 'I see that ye are dogs. I go from you to my own people—if they be my own people. The jungle is shut to me, and I must forget your talk and your companionship; but I will be more merciful than ye are. Because I was all but your brother in blood, I promise that when I am a man among men I will not betray ye to men as ye have betrayed me.' He kicked the fire with his foot, and the sparks flew up. 'There shall be no war between any of us in the Pack. But here is a debt to pay before I go.' He strode forward to where Shere Khan sat blinking stupidly at the flames, and caught him by the tuft on his chin. Bagheera followed in case of accidents. 'Up, dog!' Mowgli cried. 'Up, when a man speaks, or I will set that coat ablaze!'

Shere Khan's ears lay flat back on his head, and he shut his eyes, for the blazing branch was very near.

'This cattle-killer said he would kill me in the Council because he had not killed me when I was a cub. Thus and thus, then, do we beat dogs when we are men. Stir a whisker, Lungri, and I ram the Red Flower down thy gullet!' He beat Shere Khan over the head with the branch, and the tiger whimpered and whined in an agony of fear.

'Pah! Singed jungle-cat—go now! But remember when next I come to the Council Rock, as a man should come, it will be with Shere Khan's hide on my head. For the rest, Akela goes free to live as he pleases. Ye will *not* kill him, because that is not my will. Nor do I think that ye will sit here any longer, lolling out your tongues as though ye were somebodies, instead of dogs whom I drive out—thus! Go!' The fire was burning furiously at the end of the branch, and Mowgli struck right and left round the circle, and the wolves ran howling with the sparks burning their fur. At last there were only Akela, Bagheera, and perhaps ten wolves that had taken Mowgli's part. Then something began to hurt Mowgli inside him, as he had never been hurt in his life before, and he caught his breath and sobbed, and the tears ran down his face.

'What is it? What is it?' he said. 'I do not wish to leave the jungle, and I do not know what this is. Am I dying, Bagheera?'

'No, Little Brother. That is only tears such as men use,' said Bagheera. 'Now I know thou art a man, and a man's cub no longer. The jungle is shut indeed to thee henceforward. Let them fall, Mowgli. They are only tears.' So Mowgli sat and cried as though his heart would break; and he had never cried in all his life before.

'Now,' he said, 'I will go to men. But first I must say farewell to my mother'; and he went to the cave where she lived with Father Wolf, and he cried on her coat, while the four cubs howled miserably.

'Ye will not forget me?' said Mowgli.

'Never while we can follow a trail,' said the cubs. 'Come to the foot of the hill when thou art a man, and we will talk to thee; and we will come into the crop-lands to play with thee by night.'

'Come soon!' said Father Wolf. 'Oh, wise little frog, come again soon; for we be old, thy mother and I.'

'Come soon,' said Mother Wolf, 'little naked son of mine; for, listen, child of man, I loved thee more than ever I loved my cubs.'

'I will surely come,' said Mowgli; 'and when I come it will be to lay out Shere Khan's hide upon the Council Rock. Do not forget me! Tell them in the jungle never to forget me!'

The dawn was beginning to break when Mowgli went down the hillside alone, to meet those mysterious things that are called men.

THE LOST LEGION.

WHEN the Indian Mutiny broke out, and a little time before the siege of Delhi, a regiment of Native Irregular Horse was stationed at Peshawur on the Frontier of India. That regiment caught what John Lawrence called at the time 'the prevalent mania,' and would have thrown in its lot with the mutineers had it been allowed to do so. The chance never came, for, as the regiment swept off down south, it was headed up by a remnant of an English corps into the hills of Afghanistan, and there the newly-conquered tribesmen turned against it as wolves turn against buck. It was hunted for the sake of its arms and accoutrements from hill to hill, from ravine to ravine, up and down the dried beds of rivers and round the shoulders of bluffs, till it disappeared as water sinks in the sand—this officerless, rebel regiment. The only trace left of its existence to-day is a nominal roll drawn up in neat round hand and countersigned by an officer who called himself 'Adjutant, late ——Irregular Cavalry.' The paper is yellow with years and dirt, but on the back of it you can still read a pencil note by John Lawrence, to this effect: 'See that the two native officers who remained loyal are not deprived of their estates.—J. L.' Of six hundred and fifty sabres only two stood strain, and John Lawrence in the midst of all the agony of the first months of the mutiny found time to think about their merits.

That was more than thirty years ago, and the tribesmen

across the Afghan border who helped to annihilate the regiment are now old men. Sometimes a graybeard speaks of his share in the massacre. 'They came,' he will say, 'across the border, very proud, calling upon us to rise and kill the English, and go down to the sack of Delhi. But we who had just been conquered by the same English knew that they were over bold, and that the Government could account easily for those down-country dogs. This Hindustani regiment, therefore, we treated with fair words, and kept standing in one place till the redcoats came after them very hot and angry. Then this regiment ran forward a little more into our hills to avoid the wrath of the English, and we lay upon their flanks watching from the sides of the hills till we were well assured that their path was lost behind them. Then we came down, for we desired their clothes, and their bridles, and their rifles, and their boots—more especially their boots. That was a great killing—done slowly.' Here the old man will rub his nose, and shake his long snaky locks, and lick his bearded lips, and grin till the yellow tooth-stumps show. 'Yes, we killed them because we needed their gear, and we knew that their lives had been forfeited to God on account of their sin—the sin of treachery to the salt which they had eaten. They rode up and down the valley, stumbling and rocking in their saddles, and howling for mercy. We drove them slowly like cattle till they were all assembled in one place, the flat wide valley of Sheor Kôt. Many had died from want of water, but there still were many left, and they could not make any stand. We went among them, pulling them down with our hands two at a time, and our boys killed them who were new to the sword. My share of the plunder was such and such—so many guns, and so many saddles. The guns were good in those days. Now we steal the Government rifles, and despise smooth barrels. Yes, beyond doubt we wiped that regiment from off the face of the earth, and even the memory of the deed is now dying. But men say——'

At this point the tale would stop abruptly, and it was impossible to find out what men said across the border. The Afghans were always a secretive race, and vastly preferred doing something wicked to saying anything at all. They would be quiet and well-behaved for months, till one night, without word or warning, they would rush a police-post, cut the throats of a constable or two, dash through a village, carry away three or four women, and withdraw, in the red glare of burning thatch, driving the cattle and goats before them to their own desolate hills. The Indian Government would become almost tearful on these occasions. First it would say, 'Please be good and we'll forgive you.' The tribe concerned in the latest depredation would collectively put its thumb to its nose and answer rudely. Then the Government would say: 'Hadn't you better pay up a little money for those few corpses you left behind you the other night?' Here the tribe would temporise, and lie and bully, and some of the younger men, merely to show contempt of authority, would raid another police-post and fire into some frontier mud fort, and, if lucky, kill a real English officer. Then the Government would say: 'Observe; if you really persist in this line of conduct you will be hurt.' If the tribe knew exactly what was going on in India, it would apologise or be rude, according as it learned whether the Government was busy with other things, or able to devote its full attention to their performances. Some of the tribes knew to one corpse how far to go. Others became excited, lost their heads, and told the Government to come on. With sorrow and tears, and one eye on the British taxpayer at home, who insisted on regarding these exercises as brutal wars of annexation, the Government would prepare an expensive little field-brigade and some guns, and send all up into the hills to chase the wicked tribe out of the valleys, where the corn grew, into the hill-tops where there was nothing to eat. The tribe would turn out in full strength and enjoy the campaign, for they knew that their women would never be touched, that their wounded would be nursed, not mutilated, and that as soon as each man's bag of corn was spent they could surrender and palaver with the English General as though they had been a real enemy. Afterwards, years afterwards, they would pay the blood-money, driblet by driblet, to the Government and tell their children how they had slain the redcoats by thousands. The only drawback to this kind of picnic-war was the weakness of the redcoats for solemnly blowing up with powder their fortified towers and keeps. This the tribes always considered mean.

Chief among the leaders of the smaller tribes—the little clans who knew to a penny the expense of moving white troops against them—was a priest-bandit-chief whom we will call the Gulla Kutta Mullah. His enthusiasm for border murder as an art was almost dignified. He would cut down a mail-runner from pure wantonness, or bombard a mud fort with rifle fire when he knew that our men needed to sleep. In his leisure moments he would go on circuit among his neighbours, and try to incite other tribes to devilry. Also, he kept a kind of hotel for fellow-outlaws in his own village, which lay in a valley called Bersund. Any respectable murderer on that section of the frontier was sure to lie up at Bersund, for it was reckoned an exceedingly safe place. The sole entry to it ran through a narrow gorge which could be converted into a death-trap in five minutes. It was surrounded by high hills, reckoned inaccessible to all save born mountaineers, and here the Gulla Kutta Mullah lived in great state, the head of a colony of mud and stone huts, and in each mud hut hung some portion of a red uniform and the plunder of dead men.

The Government particularly wished for his capture, and once invited him formally to come out and be hanged on account of a few of the murders in which he had taken a direct part. He replied :—

'I am only twenty miles, as the crow flies, from your border. Come and fetch me.'

'Some day we will come,' said the Government, 'and hanged you will be.'

The Gulla Kutta Mullah let the matter from his mind. He knew that the patience of the Government was as long as a summer day; but he did not realise that its arm was as long as a winter night. Months afterwards when there was peace on the border, and all India was quiet, the Indian Government turned in its sleep and remembered the Gulla Kutta Mullah at Bersund, with his thirteen outlaws. The movement against him of one single regiment—which the telegrams would have translated as war—would have been highly impolitic. This was a time for silence and speed, and, above all, absence of bloodshed.

You must know that all along the north-west frontier of India there is spread a force of some thirty thousand foot and horse, whose duty it is quietly and unostentatiously to shepherd the tribes in front of them. They move up and down, and down and up, from one desolate little post to another; they are ready to take the field at ten minutes' notice; they are always half in and half out of a difficulty somewhere along the monotonous line; their lives are as hard as their own muscles, and the papers never say anything about them. It was from this force that the Government picked its men.

One night at a station where the mounted Night Patrol fire as they challenge, and the wheat rolls in great blue green waves under our cold northern moon, the officers were playing billiards in the mud-walled club-house, when orders came to them that they were to go on parade at once for a night-drill. They grumbled, and went to turn out their men—a hundred English troops, let us say, two hundred Goorkhas, and about a hundred cavalry of the finest native cavalry in the world.

When they were on the parade-ground, it was explained to them in whispers that they must set off at once across the hills to Bersund. The English troops were to post themselves round the hills at the side of the valley; the Goorkhas would command the gorge and the death-trap, and the cavalry would fetch a long march round and get to the back of the circle of hills, whence, if there were any difficulty, they could charge down on the Mullah's men. But orders were very strict that there should be no fighting and no noise. They were to return in the morning with every round of ammunition intact, and the Mullah and the thirteen outlaws bound in their midst. If they were successful, no one would know or care anything about their work; but failure meant probably a small border war, in which the Gulla Kutta Mullah would pose as a popular leader against a big bullying power, instead of a common border murderer.

Then there was silence, broken only by the clicking of the compass needles and snapping of watch-cases, as the heads of columns compared bearings and made appointments for the rendezvous. Five minutes later the parade-ground was empty; the green coats of the Goorkhas and the overcoats of the English troops had faded into the darkness, and the cavalry were cantering away in the face of a blinding drizzle.

What the Goorkhas and the English did will be seen later on. The heavy work lay with the horses, for they had to go far and pick their way clear of habitations. Many of the troopers were natives of that part of the world, ready and anxious to fight against their kin, and some of the officers had made private and unofficial excursions into those hills before. They crossed the border, found a dried river bed, cantered up that, walked through a stony gorge, risked crossing a low hill under cover of the darkness, skirted another hill, leaving their hoof-marks deep in some ploughed ground, felt their way along another watercourse, ran over the neck of a spur, praying that no one would hear their horses grunting, and so worked on in the rain and the darkness, till they had left Bersund and its crater of hills a little behind them, and to the left, and it was time to swing round. The ascent commanding the back of Bersund was steep, and they halted to draw breath in a broad level valley below the height. That is to say, the men reined up, but the horses, blown as they were, refused to halt. There was unchristian language, the worse for being delivered in a whisper, and you heard the saddles squeaking in the darkness as the horses plunged.

The subaltern at the rear of one troop turned in his saddle and said very softly :—

'Carter, what the blessed heavens are you doing at the rear? Bring your men up, man.'

There was no answer, till a trooper replied :—

'Carter Sahib is forward—not there. There is nothing behind us.'

'There is,' said the subaltern. 'The squadron's walking on it's own tail.'

Then the Major in command moved down to the rear swearing softly and asking for the blood of Lieutenant Halley—the subaltern who had just spoken.

'Look after your rearguard,' said the Major. 'Some of your infernal thieves have got lost. They're at the head of the squadron, and you're a several kinds of idiot.'

'Shall I tell off my men, sir?' said the subaltern sulkily, for he was feeling wet and cold.

'Tell 'em off!' said the Major. '*Whip* 'em off, by Gad! You're squandering them all over the place. There's a troop behind you *now*!'

'So I was thinking,' said the subaltern calmly. 'I have all my men here, sir. Better speak to Carter.'

'Carter Sahib sends salaam and wants to know why the regiment is stopping,' said a trooper to Lieutenant Halley.

'Where under heaven *is* Carter?' said the Major.

'Forward with his troop,' was the answer.

'Are we walking in a ring, then, or are we the centre of a blessed brigade?' said the Major.

By this time there was silence all along the column. The horses were still; but, through the drive of the fine rain, men could hear the feet of many horses moving over stony ground.

'We're being stalked,' said Lieutenant Halley.

'They've no horses here. Besides they'd have fired before this,' said the Major. 'It's—it's villagers' ponies.'

'Then our horses would have neighed and spoilt the attack long ago. They must have been near us for half an hour,' said the subaltern.

'Queer that we can't smell the horses,' said the Major, damping his finger and rubbing it on his nose as he sniffed up wind.

'Well, it's a bad start,' said the subaltern, shaking the wet from his overcoat. 'What shall we do, sir?'

'Get on,' said the Major. 'We shall catch it to-night.'

The column moved forward very gingerly for a few paces. Then there was an oath, a shower of blue sparks as shod hooves crashed on small stones, and a man rolled over with a jangle of accoutrements that would have waked the dead.

'Now we've gone and done it,' said Lieutenant Halley. 'All the hillside awake, and all the hillside to climb in the face of musketry-fire. This comes of trying to do night-hawk work.'

The trembling trooper picked himself up, and tried to explain that his horse had fallen over one of the little cairns that are built of loose stones on the spot where a man has been murdered. There was no need for reasons. The Major's big Australian charger blundered next, and the column came to a halt in what seemed to be a very graveyard of little cairns all about two feet high. The manœuvres of the squadron are not reported. Men said that it felt like mounted quadrilles without training and without the music; but at last the horses, breaking rank and choosing their own way, walked clear of the cairns, till every man of the squadron re-formed and drew rein a few yards up the slope of the hill. Then, according to Lieutenant Halley, there was another scene very like the one which has been described. The Major and Carter insisted that all the men had not joined rank, and that there were more of them in the rear clicking and blundering among the dead men's cairns. Lieutenant Halley told off his own troopers again and resigned himself to wait. Later on he told me:—

'I didn't much know, and I didn't much care what was going on. The row of that trooper falling ought to have scared half the country, and I would take my oath that we were being stalked by a full regiment in the rear, and *they* were making row enough to rouse all Afghanistan. I sat tight, but nothing happened.'

The mysterious part of the night's work was the silence on the hillside. Everybody knew that the Gulla Kutta Mullah had his outpost huts on the reverse side of the hill, and everybody expected by the time that the Major had sworn himself into a state of quiet that the watchmen there would open fire. When nothing occurred, they said that the gusts of the rain had deadened the sound of the horses, and thanked Providence. At last the Major satisfied himself (*a*) that he had left no one behind among the cairns, and (*b*) that he was not being taken in the rear by a large and powerful body of cavalry. The men's tempers were thoroughly spoiled, the horses were lathered and unquiet, and one and all prayed for the daylight.

They set themselves to climb up the hill, each man leading his mount carefully. Before they had covered the lower slopes or the breastplates had begun to tighten, a thunderstorm came up behind, rolling across the low hills and drowning any noise less than that of cannon. The first flash of the lightning showed the bare ribs of the ascent, the hill-crest standing steely blue against the black sky, the little falling lines of the rain, and, a few yards to their left flank, an Afghan watch-tower, two-storied, built of stone, and entered by a ladder from the upper story. The ladder was up, and a man with a rifle was leaning from the window. The darkness and the thunder rolled down in an instant, and, when the lull followed, a voice from the watch-tower cried, 'Who goes there?'

The cavalry were very quiet, but each man gripped his carbine and stood beside his horse. Again the voice called, 'Who goes there?' and in a louder key, 'O, brothers, give the alarm!' Now, every man in the cavalry would have died in his long boots sooner than have asked for quarter; but it is a fact that the answer to the second call was a long wail of 'Marf karo! Marf karo!' which means, 'Have mercy! Have mercy!' It came from the climbing regiment.

The cavalry stood dumbfoundered, till the big troopers had time to whisper one to another: 'Mir Khan, was that thy voice? Abdullah, didst *thou* call?' Lieutenant Halley stood beside his charger and waited. So long as no firing was going on he was content. Another flash of lightning showed the horses with heaving flanks and nodding heads, the men, white eye-balled, glaring beside them and the stone watch-tower to the left. This time there was no head at the window, and the rude iron-clamped shutter that could turn a rifle bullet was closed.

'Go on, men,' said the Major. 'Get up to the top at any rate.' The squadron toiled forward, the horses wagging their tails and the men pulling at the bridles, the stones rolling down the hillside and the sparks flying. Lieutenant Halley declares that he never heard a squadron make so much noise in his life. They scrambled up, he said, as though each horse had eight legs and a spare horse to follow him. Even then there was no sound from the watch-tower, and the men stopped exhausted on the ridge that overlooked the pit of darkness in which the village of Bersund lay. Girths were loosed, curb-chains shifted, and saddles adjusted, and the men dropped down among the stones. Whatever might happen now, they had the upper ground of any attack.

The thunder ceased, and with it the rain, and the soft thick darkness of a winter night before the dawn covered them all. Except for the sound of falling water among the ravines below, everything was still. They heard the shutter of the watch-tower below them thrown back with a clang, and the voice of the watcher calling: 'Oh, Hafiz Ullah!'

The echoes took up the call, 'La-la-la!' And an answer came from the watch-tower hidden round the curve of the hill, 'What is it, Shahbaz Khan?'

Shahbaz Khan replied in the high-pitched voice of the mountaineer: 'Hast thou seen?'

The answer came back: 'Yes. God deliver us from all evil spirits!'

There was a pause, and then: 'Hafiz Ullah, I am alone! Come to me!'

'Shahbaz Khan, I am alone also; but I dare not leave my post!'

'That is a lie; thou art afraid.'

A longer pause followed, and then: 'I am afraid. Be silent! They are below us still. Pray to God and sleep.'

The troopers listened and wondered, for they could not understand what save earth and stone could lie below the watch-towers.

Shahbaz Khan began to call again: 'They are below us. I can see them. For the pity of God come over to me, Hafiz Ullah! My father slew ten of them. Come over!'

Hafiz Ullah answered in a very loud voice, 'Mine was guiltless. Hear, ye Men of the Night, neither my father nor my blood had any part in that sin. Bear thou thy own punishment, Shahbaz Khan.'

'Oh, some one ought to stop those two chaps crowing away like cocks there,' said Lieutenant Halley, shivering under his rock.

He had hardly turned round to expose a new side of him to the rain before a bearded, long-locked, evil-smelling Afghan rushed up the hill, and tumbled into his arms. Halley sat upon him, and thrust as much of a sword-hilt as could be spared down the man's gullet. 'If you cry out, I kill you,' he said cheerfully.

The man was beyond any expression of terror. He lay and quaked, grunting. When Halley took the sword-hilt from between his teeth, he was still inarticulate, but clung to Halley's arm, feeling it from elbow to wrist.

'The Rissala! The dead Rissala!' he gasped. 'It is down there!'

'No; the Rissala, the very much alive Rissala. It is up here,' said Halley, unshipping his watering-bridle, and fastening the man's hands. 'Why were you in the towers so foolish as to let us pass?'

'The valley is full of the dead,' said the Afghan. 'It is better to fall into the hands of the English than the hands of the dead. They march to and fro below there. I saw them in the lightning.'

He recovered his composure after a little, and whispering, because Halley's pistol was at his stomach, said: 'What is this? There is no war between us now, and the Mullah will kill me for not seeing you pass!'

'Rest easy,' said Halley; 'we are coming to kill the

Mullah, if God please. His teeth have grown too long. No harm will come to thee unless the daylight shows thee as a face which is desired by the gallows for crime done. But what of the dead regiment?'

'I only kill within my own border,' said the man, immensely relieved. 'The Dead Regiment is below. The men must have passed through it on their journey—four hundred dead on horses, stumbling among their own graves, among the little heaps—dead men all, whom we slew.'

'Whew!' said Halley. 'That accounts for my cursing Carter and the Major cursing me. Four hundred sabres, eh? No wonder we thought there were a few extra men in the troop. Kurruk Shah,' he whispered to a grizzled native officer that lay within a few feet of him, 'hast thou heard anything of a dead Rissala in these hills?'

'Assuredly,' said Kurruk Shah with a grim chuckle. 'Otherwise, why did I, who have served the Queen for seven-and-twenty years, and killed many hill-dogs, shout aloud for quarter when the lightning revealed us to the watch-towers? When I was a young man I saw the killing in the valley of Sheor-Kôt there at our feet, and I know the tale that grew up therefrom. But how can the ghosts of unbelievers prevail against us who are of the Faith? Strap that dog's hands a little tighter, Sahib. An Afghan is like an eel.'

'But a dead Rissala,' said Halley, jerking his captive's wrist. 'That is foolish talk, Kurruk Shah. The dead are dead. Hold still, *sag*.' The Afghan wriggled.

'The dead are dead, and for that reason they walk at night. What need to talk? We be men; we have our eyes and ears. Thou canst both see and hear them, down the hillside,' said Kurruk Shah composedly.

Halley stared and listened long and intently. The valley was full of stifled noises, as every valley must be at night; but whether he saw or heard more than was natural Halley alone knows, and he does not choose to speak on the subject.

At last, and just before the dawn, a green rocket shot up from the far side of the valley of Bersund, at the head of the gorge, to show that the Goorkhas were in position. A red light from the infantry at left and right answered it, and the cavalry burnt a white flare. Afghans in winter are late sleepers, and it was not till full day that the Gulla Kutta Mullah's men began to straggle from their huts, rubbing their eyes. They saw men in green, and red, and brown uniforms, leaning on their arms, neatly arranged all round the crater of the village of Bersund, in a cordon that not even a wolf could have broken. They rubbed their eyes the more when a pink-faced young man, who was not even in the Army, but represented the Political Department, tripped down the hillside with two orderlies, rapped at the door of the Gulla Kutta Mullah's house, and told him quietly to step out and be tied up for safe transport. That same young man passed on through the huts, tapping here one cateran and there another lightly with his cane; and as each was pointed out, so he was tied up, staring hopelessly at the crowned heights around where the English soldiers looked down with incurious eyes. Only the Mullah tried to carry it off with curses and high words, till a soldier who was tying his hands said :—

'None o' your lip! Why didn't you come out when you was ordered, instead o' keepin' us awake all night? You're no better than my own barrack-sweeper, you white-'eaded old polyanthus! Kim up!'

Half an hour later the troops had gone away with the Mullah and his thirteen friends. The dazed villagers were looking ruefully at a pile of broken muskets and snapped swords, and wondering how in the world they had come so to miscalculate the forbearance of the Indian Government.

It was a very neat little affair, neatly carried out, and the men concerned were unofficially thanked for their services.

Yet it seems to me that much credit is also due to another regiment whose name did not appear in the brigade orders, and whose very existence is in danger of being forgotten.

NAMGAY DOOLA.

> There came to the beach a poor exile of Erin,
> The dew on his wet robe hung heavy and chill;
> Ere the steamer that brought him had passed out of hearin',
> He was Alderman Mike inthrojuicing' a bill!
>
> *American Song.*

ONCE upon a time there was a King who lived on the road to Thibet, very many miles in the Himalayas. His Kingdom was eleven thousand feet above the sea and exactly four miles square; but most of the miles stood on end owing to the nature of the country. His revenues were rather less than four hundred pounds yearly, and they were expended in the maintenance of one elephant and a standing army of five men. He was tributary to the Indian Government, who allowed him certain sums for keeping a section of the Himalaya-Thibet road in repair. He further increased his revenues by selling timber to the Railway companies; for he would cut the great deodar trees in his one forest, and they fell thundering into the Sutlej river and were swept down to the plains three hundred miles away and became railway-ties. Now and again this King, whose name does not matter, would mount a ringstraked horse and ride scores of miles to Simla-town to confer with the Lieutenant-Governor on matters of state, or to assure the Viceroy that his sword was at the service of the Queen-Empress. Then the Viceroy would cause a ruffle of drums to be sounded, and the ringstraked horse and the cavalry of the State—two men in tatters—and the herald who bore the silver stick before the King, would trot back to their own place, which lay between the tail of a heaven-climbing glacier and a dark birch-forest.

Now, from such a King, always remembering that he possessed one veritable elephant, and could count his descent for twelve hundred years, I expected, when it was my fate to wander through his dominions, no more than mere license to live.

The night had closed in rain, and rolling clouds blotted out the lights of the villages in the valley. Forty miles away, untouched by cloud or storm, the white shoulder of Donga Pa—the Mountain of the Council of the Gods—upheld the Evening Star. The monkeys sang sorrowfully to each other as they hunted for dry roosts in the fern-wreathed trees, and the last puff of the day-wind brought from the unseen villages the scent of damp wood-smoke, hot cakes, dripping undergrowth, and rotting pine-cones. That is the true smell of the Himalayas, and if once it creeps into the blood of a man, that man will at the last, forgetting all else, return to the hills to die. The clouds closed and the smell went away, and there remained nothing in all the world except chilling white mist and the boom of the Sutlej river racing through the valley below. A fat-tailed sheep, who did not want to die, bleated piteously at my tent door. He was scuffling with the Prime Minister and the Director-General of Public Education, and he was a royal gift to me and my camp servants. I expressed my thanks suitably, and asked if I might have audience of the King. The Prime Minister readjusted his turban, which had fallen off in the struggle, and assured me that the King would be very pleased to see me. Therefore, I despatched two bottles as a foretaste, and when the sheep had entered upon another incarnation went to the

King's Palace through the wet. He had sent his army to escort me, but the army stayed to talk with my cook. Soldiers are very much alike all the world over.

The Palace was a four-roomed, and whitewashed mud and timber-house, the finest in all the hills for a day's journey. The King was dressed in a purple velvet jacket, white muslin trousers, and a saffron-yellow turban of price. He gave me audience in a little carpeted room opening off the palace courtyard which was occupied by the Elephant of State. The great beast was sheeted and anchored from trunk to tail, and the curve of his back stood out grandly against the mist.

The Prime Minister and the Director-General of Public Education were present to introduce me, but all the court had been dismissed, lest the two bottles aforesaid should corrupt their morals. The King cast a wreath of heavy-scented flowers round my neck as I bowed, and inquired how my honoured presence had the felicity to be. I said that through seeing his auspicious countenance the mists of the night had turned into sunshine, and that by reason of his beneficent sheep his good deeds would be remembered by the Gods. He said that since I had set my magnificent foot in his Kingdom the crops would probably yield seventy per cent. more than the average. I said that the fame of the King had reached to the four corners of the earth, and that the nations gnashed their teeth when they heard daily of the glories of his realm and the wisdom of his moon-like Prime Minister and lotus-like Director-General of Public Education.

Then we sat down on clean white cushions, and I was at the King's right hand. Three minutes later he was telling me that the state of the maize crop was something disgraceful, and that the Railway companies would not pay him enough for his timber. The talk shifted to and fro with the bottles, and we discussed very many stately things, and the King became confidential on the subject of Government generally. Most of all he dwelt on the shortcomings of one of his subjects, who, from all I could gather, had been paralysing the executive.

'In the old days,' said the King, 'I could have ordered the Elephant yonder to trample him to death. Now I must e'en send him seventy miles across the hills to be tried, and his keep would be upon the State. The Elephant eats everything.'

'What be the man's crimes, Rajah Sahib?' said I.

'Firstly, he is an outlander and no man of mine own people. Secondly, since of my favour I gave him land upon his first coming, he refuses to pay revenue. Am I not the lord of the earth, above and below, entitled by right and custom to one-eighth of the crop? Yet this devil, establishing himself, refuses to pay a single tax; and he brings a poisonous spawn of babes.'

'Cast him into jail,' I said.

'Sahib,' the King answered, shifting a little on the cushions, 'once and only once in these forty years sickness came upon me so that I was not able to go abroad. In that hour I made a vow to my God that I would never again cut man or woman from the light of the sun and the air of God; for I perceived the nature of the punishment. How can I break my vow? Were it only the lopping of a hand or a foot I should not delay. But even that is impossible now that the English have rule. One or another of my people'—he looked obliquely at the Director-General of Public Education—'would at once write a letter to the Viceroy, and perhaps I should be deprived of my ruffle of drums.'

He unscrewed the mouthpiece of his silver water-pipe, fitted a plain amber mouthpiece, and passed his pipe to me. 'Not content with refusing revenue,' he continued, 'this outlander refuses also the *begar*' (this was the corvée or forced labour on the roads) 'and stirs my people up to the like treason. Yet he is, when he wills, an expert log-snatcher. There is none better or bolder among my people to clear a block of the river when the logs stick fast.'

'But he worships strange Gods,' said the Prime Minister deferentially.

'For that I have no concern,' said the King, who was as tolerant as Akbar in matters of belief. 'To each man his own God and the fire or Mother Earth for us all at last. It is the rebellion that offends me.'

'The King has an army,' I suggested. 'Has not the King burned the man's house and left him naked to the night dews?'

'Nay, a hut is a hut, and it holds the life of a man. But once, I sent my army against him when his excuses became wearisome: of their heads he brake three across the top with a stick. The other two men ran away. Also the guns would not shoot.'

I had seen the equipment of the infantry. One-third of it was an old muzzle-loading fowling-piece, with a ragged rust-hole where the nipples should have been, one-third a wire-bound match-lock with a worm-eaten stock, and one-third a four-bore flint duck-gun without a flint.

'But it is to be remembered,' said the King, reaching out for the bottle, 'that he is a very expert log-snatcher and a man of a merry face. What shall I do to him, Sahib?'

This was interesting. The timid hill-folk would as soon have refused taxes to their King as revenues to their Gods.

'If it be the King's permission,' I said, 'I will not strike my tents till the third day and I will see this man. The mercy of the King is God-like, and rebellion is like unto the sin of witchcraft. Moreover, both the bottles and another be empty.'

'You have my leave to go,' said the King.

Next morning a crier went through the State proclaiming that there was a log-jam on the river and that it behoved all loyal subjects to remove it. The people poured down from their villages to the moist, warm valley of poppy-fields; and the King and I went with them. Hundreds of dressed deodar-logs had caught on a snag of rock, and the river was bringing down more logs every minute to complete the blockade. The water snarled and wrenched and worried at the timber, and the population of the State began prodding the nearest logs with a pole in the hope of starting a general movement. Then there went up a shout of 'Namgay Doola! Namgay Doola!' and a large red-haired villager hurried up, stripping off his clothes as he ran.

'That is he. That is the rebel,' said the King. 'Now will the dam be cleared.'

'But why has he red hair?' I asked, since red hair among hill-folks is as common as blue or green.

'He is an outlander,' said the King. 'Well done! Oh, well done!'

Namgay Doola had scrambled out on the jam and was clawing out the butt of a log with a rude sort of boathook. It slid forward slowly as an alligator moves, three or four others followed it, and the green water spouted through the gaps they had made. Then the villagers howled and shouted and scrambled across the logs, pulling and pushing the obstinate timber, and the red head of Namgay Doola was chief among them all. The logs swayed and chafed and groaned as fresh consignments from upstream battered the now weakening dam. All gave way at last in a smother of foam, racing logs, bobbing black heads and confusion indescribable. The river tossed everything before it. I saw the red head go down with the last remnants of the jam and disappear between the great grinding tree trunks. It rose close to the bank and blowing like a grampus. Namgay Doola wrung the water out of his eyes and made obeisance to the King. I had time to observe him closely. The virulent redness of his shock head and beard was most startling; and in the thicket of hair wrinkled above high cheek bones shone two very merry blue eyes. He was indeed an outlander, but yet a Thibetan in language, habit, and attire. He spoke the Lepcha dialect with an indescribable softening of the gutturals. It was not so much a lisp as an accent.

'Whence comest thou?' I asked.

'From Thibet.' He pointed across the hills and grinned. That grin went straight to my heart. Mechanically I held out my hand and Namgay Doola shook it. No pure Thibetan would have understood the meaning of the gesture. He went away to look for his clothes, and as he climbed back to his village, I heard a joyous yell that seemed unaccountably familiar. It was the whooping of Namgay Doola.

'You see now,' said the King, 'why I would not kill him. He is a bold man among my logs, but,' and he shook his head like a schoolmaster, 'I know that before long there will be complaints of him in the court. Let us return to the Palace and do justice.' It was that King's custom to judge his subjects every day between eleven and three o'clock. I saw him decide equitably in weighty matters of trespass, slander, and a little wife-stealing. Then his brow clouded and he summoned me.

'Again it is Namgay Doola,' he said despairingly. 'Not content with refusing revenue on his own part, he has bound half his village by an oath to the like treason. Never before has such a thing befallen me! Nor are my taxes heavy.'

A rabbit-faced villager, with a blush-rose stuck behind his ear, advanced trembling. He had been in the conspiracy, but had told everything and hoped for the King's favour.

'O King,' said I. 'If it be the King's will let this matter stand over till the morning. Only the Gods can do right swiftly, and it may be that yonder villager has lied.'

'Nay, for I know the nature of Namgay Doola; but since a guest asks let the matter remain. Wilt thou speak harshly to this red-headed outlander. He may listen to thee.'

I made an attempt that very evening, but for the life of me I could not keep my countenance. Namgay Doola grinned persuasively, and began to tell me about a big brown bear in a poppy-field by the river. Would I care to shoot it? I spoke austerely on the sin of conspiracy, and the certainty of punishment. Namgay Doola's face clouded for a moment. Shortly afterwards he withdrew from my tent, and I heard him singing to himself softly among the pines. The words were unintelligible to me, but the tune, like his liquid insinuating speech, seemed the ghost of something strangely familiar.

> Dir hané mard-i-yemen dir
> To weeree ala gee,

sang Namgay Doola again and again, and I racked my brain for that lost tune. It was not till after dinner that I discovered some one had cut a square foot of velvet from the centre of my best camera-cloth. This made me so angry that I wandered down the valley in the hope of meeting the big brown bear. I could hear him grunting like a discontented pig in the poppy-field, and I waited shoulder deep in the dew-dripping Indian corn to catch him after his meal. The moon was at full and drew out the rich scent of the tasselled crop. Then I heard the anguished bellow of a Himalayan cow, one of the little black crummies no bigger than Newfoundland dogs. Two shadows that looked like a bear and her cub hurried past me. I was in act to fire when I saw that they had each a brilliant red head. The lesser animal was trailing some rope behind it that left a dark track on the path. They passed within six feet of me, and the shadow of the moonlight lay velvet-black on their faces. Velvet-black was exactly the word, for by all the powers of moonlight they were masked in the velvet of my camera cloth! I marvelled and went to bed.

Next morning the Kingdom was in uproar. Namgay Doola, men said, had gone forth in the night and with a sharp knife had cut off the tail of a cow belonging to the rabbit-faced villager who had betrayed him. It was sacrilege unspeakable against the Holy Cow. The State desired his blood, but he had retreated into his hut, barricaded the doors and windows with big stones, and defied the world.

The King and I and the Populace approached the hut cautiously. There was no hope of capturing the man without loss of life, for from a hole in the wall projected the muzzle of an extremely well-cared-for gun—the only gun in the State that could shoot. Namgay Doola had narrowly missed a villager just before we came up. The Standing Army stood. It could do no more, for when it advanced pieces of sharp shale flew from the windows. To these were added from time to time showers of scalding water. We saw red heads bobbing up and down in the hut. The family of Namgay Doola were aiding their sire, and blood-curdling yells of defiance were the only answers to our prayers.

'Never,' said the King, puffing, 'has such a thing befallen my State. Next year I will certainly buy a little cannon.' He looked at me imploringly.

'Is there any priest in the Kingdom to whom he will listen?' said I, for a light was beginning to break upon me.

'He worships his own God,' said the Prime Minister. We can starve him out.'

'Let the white man approach,' said Namgay Doola from within. All others I will kill. Send me the white man.'

The door was thrown open and I entered the smoky interior of a Thibetan hut crammed with children. And every child had flaming red hair. A raw cow's tail lay on the floor, and by its side two pieces of black velvet—my black velvet—rudely hacked into the semblance of masks.

'And what is this shame, Namgay Doola?' said I.

He grinned more winningly than ever. 'There is no shame,' said he. 'I did but cut off the tail of that man's cow. He betrayed me. I was minded to shoot him, Sahib. But not to death. Indeed not to death. Only in the legs.'

'And why at all, since it is the custom to pay revenue to the King? Why at all?'

'By the God of my father I cannot tell,' said Namgay Doola.

'And who was thy father?'

'The same that had this gun.' He showed me his weapon—a Tower musket bearing date 1832 and the stamp of the Honourable East India Company.

'And thy father's name?' said I.

'Timlay Doola,' said he. 'At the first, I being then a little child, it is in my mind that he wore a red coat.'

'Of that I have no doubt. But repeat the name of thy father thrice or four times.'

He obeyed, and I understood whence the puzzling accent in his speech came. 'Thimla Dhula,' said he excitedly. 'To this hour I worship his God.'

'May I see that God?'

'In a little while—at twilight time.'

'Rememberest thou aught of thy father's speech?'

'It is long ago. But there is one word which he said often. Thus "*Shun.*" Then I and my brethren stood upon our feet, our hands to our sides. Thus.'

'Even so. And what was thy mother?'

'A woman of the hills. We be Lepchas of Darjeeling, but me they call an outlander because my hair is as thou seest.'

The Thibetan woman, his wife, touched him on the arm gently. The long parley outside the fort had lasted far into the day. It was now close upon twilight—the hour of the Angelus. Very solemnly, the red-headed brats rose from the floor and formed a semicircle. Namgay Doola laid his gun against the wall, lighted a little oil lamp, and set it before a recess in the wall. Pulling aside a curtain of dirty cloth he revealed a worn brass crucifix leaning against the helmet-badge of a long forgotten East India regiment. 'Thus did my father,' he said, crossing himself clumsily. The wife and children followed suit. Then all together they struck up the wailing chant that I heard on the hillside—

> Dir hané mard-i-yemen dir
> To weeree ala gee.

I was puzzled no longer. Again and again they crooned as if their hearts would break, their version of the chorus of the *Wearing of the Green*—

> They're hanging men and women too,
> For the wearing of the green.

A diabolical inspiration came to me. One of the brats, a boy about eight years old, was watching me as he sang. I pulled out a rupee, held the coin between finger and thumb, and looked—only looked—at the gun against the wall. A grin of brilliant and perfect comprehension overspread the face of the child. Never for an instant stopping the song he held out his hand for the money, and then slid the gun to my hand. I might have shot Namgay Doola as he chanted. But I was satisfied. The blood instinct of the race held true. Namgay Doola drew the curtain across the recess. Angelus was over.

'Thus my father sang. There was much more, but I have forgotten, and I do not know the purport of these words, but it may be that the God will understand. I am not of this people, and I will not pay revenue.'

'And why?'

Again that soul-compelling grin. 'What occupation would be to me between crop and crop? It is better than scaring bears. But these people do not understand.' He picked the masks from the floor, and looked in my face as simply as a child.

'By what road didst thou attain knowledge to make these devilries?' I said, pointing.

'I cannot tell. I am but a Lepcha of Darjeeling, and yet the stuff——'

'Which thou hast stolen.'

'Nay, surely. Did I steal? I desired it so. The stuff —the stuff—what else should I have done with the stuff?' He twisted the velvet between his fingers.

'But the sin of maiming the cow—consider that?'

'That is true; but oh, Sahib, that man betrayed me and I had no thought—but the heifer's tail waved in the moonlight and I had my knife. What else should I have done? The tail came off ere I was aware. Sahib, thou knowest more than I.'

'That is true,' said I. 'Stay within the door. I go to speak to the King.'

The population of the State were ranged on the hillsides. I went forth and spoke to the King.

'Oh King,' said I. 'Touching this man there be two courses open to thy wisdom. Thou canst either hang him from a tree, he and his brood, till there remains no hair that is red within the land.'

'Nay,' said the King. 'Why should I hurt the little children?'

They had poured out of the hut door and were making plump obeisance to everybody. Namgay Doola waited with his gun across his arm.

'Or thou canst, discarding the impiety of the cow-maiming, raise him to honour in thy Army. He comes of a race that will not pay revenue. A red flame is in his blood which comes out at the top of his head in that glowing hair. Make him chief of the Army. Give him honour as may befall, and full allowance of work, but look to it, O King, that neither he nor his hold a foot of earth from thee henceforward. Feed him with words and favour, and also liquor from certain bottles that thou knowest of, and he will be a bulwark of defence. But deny him even a tuft of grass for his own. This is the nature that God has given him. Moreover he has brethren——'

The State groaned unanimously.

'But if his brethren come, they will surely fight with each other till they die; or else the one will always give information concerning the other. Shall he be of thy Army, O King? Choose.'

The King bowed his head, and I said, 'Come forth, Namgay Doola, and command the King's Army. Thy name shall no more be Namgay in the mouths of men, but Patsay Doola, for as thou hast said, I know.'

Then Namgay Doola, new christened Patsay Doola, son of Timlay Doola, which is Tim Doolan gone very wrong indeed, clasped the King's feet, cuffed the standing Army, and hurried in an agony of contrition from temple to temple, making offerings for the sin of cattle maiming.

And the King was so pleased with my perspicacity that he offered to sell me a village for twenty pounds sterling. But I buy no villages in the Himalayas so long as one red head flares between the tail of the heaven-climbing glacier and the dark birch-forest.

I know that breed.

A GERM-DESTROYER

Pleasant it is for the Little Tin Gods
  When great Jove nods;
But Little Tin Gods make their little mistakes
In missing the hour when great Jove wakes.

As a general rule, it is inexpedient to meddle with questions of State in a land where men are highly paid to work them out for you. This tale is a justifiable exception.

Once in every five years, as you know, we indent for a new Viceroy; and each Viceroy imports, with the rest of his baggage, a Private Secretary, who may or may not be the real Viceroy, just as Fate ordains. Fate looks after the Indian Empire because it is so big and so helpless.

There was a Viceroy once who brought out with him a turbulent Private Secretary—a hard man with a soft manner and a morbid passion for work. This Secretary was called Wonder—John Fennil Wonder. The Viceroy possessed no name—nothing but a string of counties and two-thirds of the alphabet after them. He said, in confidence, that he was the electro-plated figurehead of a golden administration, and he watched in a dreamy, amused way Wonder's attempts to draw matters which were entirely outside his province into his own hands. 'When we are all cherubims together,' said His Excellency once, 'my dear, good friend Wonder will head the conspiracy for plucking out Gabriel's tail feathers or stealing Peter's keys. *Then* I shall report him.'

But, though the Viceroy did nothing to check Wonder's officiousness, other people said unpleasant things. May be the Members of Council began it; but finally all Simla agreed that there was 'too much Wonder and too little Viceroy' in that rule. Wonder was always quoting 'His Excellency.' It was 'His Excellency this,' 'His Excellency that,' 'In the opinion of His Excellency,' and so on. The Viceroy smiled; but he did not heed. He said that, so long as his old men squabbled with his 'dear, good Wonder,' they might be induced to leave the Immemorial East in peace.

'No wise man has a Policy,' said the Viceroy. 'A Policy is the blackmail levied on the Fool by the Unforeseen. I am not the former, and I do not believe in the latter.'

I do not quite see what this means, unless it refers to an Insurance Policy. Perhaps it was the Viceroy's way of saying, 'Lie low.'

That season came up to Simla one of these crazy people with only a single idea. These are the men who make things move; but they are not nice to talk to. This man's name was Mellish, and he had lived for fifteen years on land of his own, in Lower Bengal, studying cholera. He held that cholera was a germ that propagated itself as it flew through a muggy atmosphere; and stuck in the branches of trees like a wool-flake. The germ could be rendered sterile, he said, by 'Mellish's Own Invincible Fumigatory'—a heavy violet-black powder—'the result of fifteen years' scientific investigation, Sir!'

Inventors seem very much alike as a caste. They talk loudly, especially about 'conspiracies of monopolists'; they beat upon the table with their fists; and they secrete fragments of their inventions about their persons.

Mellish said that there was a Medical 'Ring' at Simla, headed by the Surgeon-General, who was in league, apparently, with all the Hospital Assistants in the Empire. I forget exactly how he proved it, but it had something to do with 'skulking up to the Hills'; and what Mellish wanted was the independent evidence of the Viceroy—'Steward of our Most Gracious Majesty the Queen, Sir.' So Mellish went up to Simla, with eighty-four pounds of Fumigatory in his trunk, to speak to the Viceroy and to show him the merits of the invention.

But it is easier to see a Viceroy than to talk to him, unless you chance to be as important as Mellishe of Madras. He was a six-thousand-rupee man, so great that his daughters never 'married.' They 'contracted alliances.' He himself was not paid. He 'received emoluments,' and his journeys about the country were 'tours of observation.' His business was to stir up the people in Madras with a long pole—as you stir up tench in a pond—and the people had to come up out of their comfortable old ways and gasp—'This is Enlightenment and Progress. Isn't it fine!' Then they give Mellishe statues and jasmine garlands, in the hope of getting rid of him.

Mellishe came up to Simla 'to confer with the Viceroy.' That was one of his perquisites. The Viceroy knew nothing of Mellishe except that he was 'one of those middle-class deities who seem necessary to the spiritual comfort of this Paradise of the Middle-classes,' and that, in all probability he had 'suggested, designed, founded, and endowed all the public institutions in Madras.' Which proves that His Excellency, though dreamy, had experience of the ways of six-thousand-rupee men.

Mellishe's name was E. Mellishe, and Mellish's was E. S. Mellish, and they were both staying at the same hotel, and the Fate that looks after the Indian Empire ordained that Wonder should blunder and drop the final '*e*'; that the Chaprassi should help him, and that the note which ran—

Dear Mr. Mellish,—Can you set aside your other engagements, and lunch with us at two to-morrow? His Excellency has an hour at your disposal then, should be given to Mellish with the Fumigatory. He nearly wept with pride and delight, and at the appointed hour cantered to Peterhoff, a big paper-bag full of the Fumigatory in his coat-tail pockets. He had his chance, and he meant to make the most of it. Mellishe of Madras had been so portentously solemn about his 'conference,' that Wonder had arranged for a private tiffin,—no A.-D.-C.'s, no Wonder, no one but the Viceroy, who said plaintively that he feared being left alone with unmuzzled autocrats like the great Mellishe of Madras.

But his guest did not bore the Viceroy. On the contrary, he amused him. Mellish was nervously anxious to go straight to his Fumigatory, and talked at random until tiffin was over and His Excellency asked him to smoke. The Viceroy was pleased with Mellish because he did not talk 'shop.'

As soon as the cheroots were lit, Mellish spoke like a man; beginning with his cholera-theory, reviewing his fifteen years' 'scientific labours,' the machinations of the 'Simla Ring,' and the excellence of his Fumigatory, while the Viceroy watched him between half-shut eyes and thought—'Evidently this is the wrong tiger; but it is an original animal.' Mellish's hair was standing on end with excitement, and he stammered. He began groping in his coat-tails and, before the Viceroy knew what was about to happen, he had tipped a bagful of his powder into the big silver ash-tray.

'J-j-judge for yourself, Sir,' said Mellish. 'Y' Excellency shall judge for yourself! Absolutely infallible, on my honour.'

He plunged the lighted end of his cigar into the powder, which began to smoke like a volcano, and send up fat, greasy wreaths of copper-coloured smoke. In five seconds the room was filled with a most pungent and sickening stench—a reek that took fierce hold of the trap of your windpipe and shut it. The powder hissed and fizzed, and sent out blue and green sparks, and the smoke rose till you could neither see, nor breathe, nor gasp. Mellish, however, was used to it.

'Nitrate of strontia,' he shouted; 'baryta, bone-meal, *etcetera*! Thousand cubic feet smoke per cubic inch. Not a germ could live—not a germ, Y' Excellency!'

But His Excellency had fled, and was coughing at the foot of the stairs, while all Peterhoff hummed like a hive. Red Lancers came in, and the head Chaprassi who speaks English came in, and mace-bearers came in, and ladies ran downstairs screaming, 'Fire'; for the smoke was drifting through the house and oozing out of the windows, and bellying along the verandahs, and wreathing and writhing across the gardens. No one could enter the room where Mellish was lecturing on his Fumigatory till that unspeakable powder had burned itself out.

Then an Aide-de-Camp, who desired the V.C., rushed through the rolling clouds and hauled Mellish into the hall. The Viceroy was prostrate with laughter, and could only waggle his hands feebly at Mellish, who was shaking a fresh bagful of powder at him.

'Glorious! Glorious!' sobbed His Excellency. 'Not a germ, as you justly observe, could exist! I can swear it. A magnificent success!'

Then he laughed till the tears came, and Wonder, who had caught the real Mellishe snorting on the Mall, entered and was deeply shocked at the scene. But the Viceroy was delighted, because he saw that Wonder would presently depart. Mellish with the Fumigatory was also pleased, for he felt that he had smashed the Simla Medical 'Ring.'

. . . . . .

Few men could tell a story like His Excellency when he took the trouble, and his account of 'my dear, good Wonder's friend with the powder' went the round of

Simla, and flippant folk made Wonder unhappy by their remarks.

But His Excellency told the tale once too often—for Wonder. As he meant to do. It was at a Seepee Picnic. Wonder was sitting just behind the Viceroy.

'And I really thought for a moment,' wound up His Excellency, 'that my dear, good Wonder had hired an assassin to clear his way to the throne!'

Every one laughed; but there was a delicate sub-tinkle in the Viceroy's tone which Wonder understood. He found that his health was giving way; and the Viceroy allowed him to go, and presented him with a flaming 'character' for use at Home among big people.

'My fault entirely,' said His Excellency, in after seasons, with a twinkle in his eye. 'My inconsistency must always have been distasteful to such a masterly man.'

'TIGER-TIGER!'

What of the hunting, hunter bold?
  Brother, the watch was long and cold.
What of the quarry ye went to kill?
  Brother, he crops in the jungle still.
Where is the power that made your pride?
  Brother, it ebbs from my flank and side.
Where is the haste that ye hurry by?
  Brother, I go to my lair to die.

WHEN Mowgli left the wolf's cave after the fight with the Pack at the Council Rock, he went down to the ploughed lands where the villagers lived, but he would not stop there because it was too near to the jungle, and he knew that he had made at least one bad enemy at the Council. So he hurried on, keeping to the rough road that ran down the valley, and followed it at a steady jog-trot for nearly twenty miles, till he came to a country that he did not know. The valley opened out into a great plain dotted over with rocks and cut up by ravines. At one end stood a little village, and at the other the thick jungle came down in a sweep to the grazing-grounds, and stopped there as though it had been cut off with a hoe. All over the plain, cattle and buffaloes were grazing, and when the little boys in charge of the herds saw Mowgli they shouted and ran away, and the yellow pariah dogs that hang about every Indian village barked. Mowgli walked on, for he was feeling hungry, and when he came to the village gate he saw the big thornbush that was drawn up before the gate at twilight, pushed to one side.

'Umph!' he said, for he had come across more than one such barricade in his night rambles after things to eat. 'So men are afraid of the People of the Jungle here also.' He sat down by the gate, and when a man came out he stood up, opened his mouth, and pointed down it to show that he wanted food. The man stared, and ran back up the one street of the village, shouting for the priest, who was a big, fat man dressed in white, with a red and yellow mark on his forehead. The priest came to the gate, and with him at least a hundred people, who stared and talked and shouted and pointed at Mowgli.

'They have no manners, these Men Folk,' said Mowgli to himself. 'Only the gray ape would behave as they do.' So he threw back his long hair and frowned at the crowd.

'What is there to be afraid of?' said the priest. 'Look at the marks on his arms and legs. They are the bites of wolves. He is but a wolf-child run away from the jungle.'

Of course, in playing together, the cubs had often nipped Mowgli harder than they intended, and there were white scars all over his arms and legs. But he would have been the last person in the world to call these bites, for he knew what real biting meant.

'*Arré! arré!*' said two or three women together. 'To be bitten by wolves, poor child! He is a handsome boy. He has eyes like red fire. By my honour, Messua, he is not unlike thy boy that was taken by the tiger.'

'Let me look,' said a woman with heavy copper rings on her wrists and ankles, and she peered at Mowgli under the palm of her hand. 'Indeed he is not. He is thinner, but he has the very look of my boy.'

The priest was a clever man, and he knew that Messua was wife to the richest villager in the place. So he looked up at the sky for a minute, and said solemnly: 'What the jungle has taken the jungle has restored. Take the boy into thy house, my sister, and forget not to honour the priest who sees so far into the lives of men.'

'By the Bull that bought me,' said Mowgli to himself, 'but all this talking is like another looking over by the Pack! Well, if I am a man, a man I must be.'

The crowd parted as the woman beckoned Mowgli to her hut, where there was a red lacquered bedstead, a great earthen grain-chest with funny raised patterns on it, half a dozen copper cooking-pots, an image of a Hindu god in a little alcove, and on the wall a real looking-glass, such as they sell at the country fairs for eight cents.

She gave him a long drink of milk and some bread, and then she laid her hand on his head and looked into his eyes; for she thought perhaps that he might be her real son come back from the jungle where the tiger had taken him. So she said: 'Nathoo, O Nathoo!' Mowgli did not show that he knew the name. 'Dost thou not remember the day when I gave thee thy new shoes?' She touched his foot, and it was almost as hard as horn. 'No,' she said, sorrowfully; 'those feet have never worn shoes, but thou art very like my Nathoo, and thou shalt be my son.'

Mowgli was uneasy, because he had never been under a roof before; but as he looked at the thatch, he saw that he could tear it out any time if he wanted to get away, and that the window had no fastenings. 'What is the good of a man,' he said to himself at last, 'if he does not understand man's talk? Now I am as silly and dumb as a man would be with us in the jungle. I must speak their talk.'

He had not learned while he was with the wolves to imitate the challenge of bucks in the jungle and the grunt of the little wild pig for fun. So, as soon as Messua pronounced a word Mowgli would imitate it almost perfectly, and before dark he had learned the name of many things in the hut.

There was a difficulty at bedtime, because Mowgli would not sleep under anything that looked so like a panther-trap as that hut, and when they shut the door he went through the window. 'Give him his will,' said Messua's husband. 'Remember he can never till now have slept on a bed. If he is indeed sent in the place of our son he will not run away.'

So Mowgli stretched himself in some long clean grass at the edge of the field, but before he had closed his eyes a soft gray nose poked him under the chin.

'Phew!' said Gray Brother (he was the eldest of Mother Wolf's cubs). 'This is a poor reward for following thee twenty miles. Thou smellest of wood-smoke and cattle—altogether like a man already. Wake, Little Brother; I bring news.'

'Are all well in the jungle?' said Mowgli, hugging him.

'All except the wolves that were burned with the Red Flower. Now, listen. Shere Khan has gone away to hunt far off till his coat grows again, for he is badly singed. When he returns he swears that he will lay thy bones in the Waingunga.'

'There are two words to that. I also have made a little promise. But news is always good. I am tired to-night,—very tired with new things, Gray Brother,—but bring me the news always.'

'Thou wilt not forget that thou art a wolf? Men will not make thee forget?' said Gray Brother, anxiously.

'Never. I will always remember that I love thee and all in our cave; but also I will always remember that I have been cast out of the Pack.'

'And that thou may'st be cast out of another pack. Men are only men, Little Brother, and their talk is like the talk of frogs in a pond. When I come down here again, I will wait for thee in the bamboos at the edge of the grazing ground.'

For three months after that night Mowgli hardly ever left the village gate, he was so busy learning the ways and customs of men. First he had to wear a cloth round him, which annoyed him horribly; and then he had to learn about money, which he did not in the least understand, and about ploughing, of which he did not see the use. Then the little children in the village made him very angry. Luckily, the Law of the Jungle had taught him to keep his temper, for in the jungle, life and food depend on keeping your temper; but when they made fun of him because he would not play games or fly kites, or because he mispronounced some word, only the knowledge that it was unsportsmanlike to kill little naked cubs kept him from picking them up and breaking them in two. He did not know his own strength in the least. In the jungle he knew he was weak compared with the beasts, but in the village, people said that he was as strong as a bull. He certainly had no notion of what fear was, for when the village priest told him that the god in the temple would be angry with him if he ate the priest's mangoes, he picked up the image, brought it over to the priest's house, and asked the priest to make the god angry and he would be happy to fight him. It was a horrible scandal, but the priest hushed it up, and Messua's husband paid much good silver to comfort the god. And Mowgli had not the faintest idea of the difference that caste makes between man and man. When the potter's donkey slipped in the clay-pit, Mowgli hauled it out by the tail, and helped to stack the pots for their journey to the market at Khanhiwara. That was very shocking, too, for the potter is a low-caste man, and his donkey is worse. When the priest scolded him, Mowgli threatened to put him on the donkey, too, and the priest told Messua's husband that Mowgli had better be set to work as soon as possible; and the village headman told Mowgli that he would have to go out with the buffaloes next day, and herd them while they grazed. No one was more pleased than Mowgli; and that night, because he had been appointed a servant of the village, as it were, he went off to a circle that met every evening on a masonry platform under a great fig-tree. It was the village club, and the head-man and the watchman and the barber, who knew all the gossip of the village, and old Buldeo, the village hunter, who had a Tower musket, met and smoked. The monkeys sat and talked in the upper branches, and there was a hole under the platform where a cobra lived, and he had his little platter of milk every night because he was sacred; and the old men sat around the tree and talked, and pulled at the big *huqas* (the water-pipes) till far into the night. They told wonderful tales of gods and men and ghosts; and Buldeo told even more wonderful ones of the ways of beasts in the jungle, till the eyes of the children sitting outside the circle bulged out of their heads. Most of the tales were about animals, for the jungle was always at their door. The deer and the wild pig grubbed up their crops, and now and again the tiger carried off a man at twilight, within sight of the village gates.

Mowgli, who naturally knew something about what they were talking of, had to cover his face not to show that he was laughing, while Buldeo, the Tower musket across his knees, climbed on from one wonderful story to another, and Mowgli's shoulders shook.

Buldeo was explaining how the tiger that had carried away Messua's son was a ghost-tiger, and his body was inhabited by the ghost of a wicked, old money-lender, who had died some years ago. 'And I know that this is true,' he said, 'because Purun Dass always limped from the blow that he got in a riot when his account-books were burned, and the tiger that I speak of *he* limps, too, for the tracks of his pads are unequal.'

'True, true, that must be the truth,' said the graybeards, nodding together.

'Are all these tales such cobwebs and moontalk?' said Mowgli. 'That tiger limps because he was born lame, as every one knows. To talk of the soul of a money-lender in a beast that never had the courage of a jackal is child's talk.'

Buldeo was speechless with surprise for a moment, and the head-man stared.

'Oho! It is the jungle brat, is it?' said Buldeo. 'If thou art so wise, better bring his hide to Khanhiwara, for the Government has set a hundred rupees on his life. Better still, talk not when thy elders speak.'

Mowgli rose to go. 'All the evening I have lain here listening,' he called back, over his shoulder, 'and, except once or twice, Buldeo has not said one word of truth concerning the jungle, which is at his very doors. How then shall I believe the tales of ghosts and gods, and goblins which he says he has seen?'

'It is full time that boy went to herding,' said the head-man, while Buldeo puffed and snorted at Mowgli's impertinence.

The custom of most Indian villages is for a few boys to take the cattle and buffaloes out to graze in the early morning, and bring them back at night; and the very cattle that would trample a white man to death allow themselves to be banged and bullied and shouted at by children that hardly come up to their noses. So long as the boys keep with the herds they are safe, for not even the tiger will charge a mob of cattle. But if they straggle to pick flowers or hunt lizards, they are sometimes carried off. Mowgli went through the village street in the dawn, sitting on the back of Rama, the great herd bull; and the slaty-blue buffaloes, with their long, backward-sweeping horns and savage eyes, rose out of their byres, one by one, and followed him, and Mowgli made it very clear to the children with him that he was the master. He beat the buffaloes with a long, polished bamboo, and told Kamya, one of the boys, to graze the cattle by themselves, while he went on with the buffaloes, and to be very careful not to stray away from the herd.

An Indian grazing-ground is all rocks, and scrubs, and tussocks, and little ravines, among which the herds scatter and disappear. The buffaloes generally keep to the pools and muddy places, where they lie wallowing or basking in the warm mud for hours. Mowgli drove them on to the edge of the plain where the Waingunga came out of the jungle; then he dropped from Rama's neck, trotted off to a bamboo clump and found Gray Brother. 'Ah,' said Gray Brother, 'I have waited here very many days. What is the meaning of this cattle-herding work?'

'It is an order,' said Mowgli; 'I am a village herd for a while. What news of Shere Khan?'

'He has come back to this country, and has waited here a long time for thee. Now he has gone off again, for the game is scarce. But he means to kill thee.'

'Very good,' said Mowgli. 'So long as he is away do thou or one of the four brothers sit on that rock, so that I can see thee as I come out of the village. When he comes back wait for me in the ravine by the *dhâk*-tree in the centre of the plain. We need not walk into Shere Khan's mouth.'

Then Mowgli picked out a shady place, and lay down and slept while the buffaloes grazed round him. Herding, in India, is one of the laziest things in the world. The cattle move and crunch, and lie down, and move on again, and they do not even low. They only grunt, and the buffaloes very seldom say anything, but get down into the muddy pools one after another, and work their way into the mud till only their noses and staring china-blue eyes show above the surface, and then they lie like logs. The sun makes the rocks dance in the heat, and the herd-children hear one kite (never any more) whistling almost out of sight overhead, and they know that if they died, or a cow died, that kite would sweep down, and the next kite miles away would see him drop and follow, and the next, and the next, and almost before they were dead there would be a score of hungry kites come out of nowhere. Then they sleep and wake and sleep again, and weave little baskets of dried grass and put grasshoppers in them, or catch two praying mantises and make them fight; or string a necklace of red and black jungle-nuts, or watch a lizard basking on a rock, or a snake hunting a frog near the wallows. Then they sing long, long songs with odd native quavers at the end of them, and the day seems longer than most people's whole lives, and perhaps they make a mud castle with mud figures of men and horses and buffaloes, and put reeds into the men's hands, and pretend that they are kings and the figures are their armies, or that they are gods to be worshipped. Then evening comes and the children call, and the buffaloes lumber up out of the sticky mud with noises like gunshots going off one after the other, and they all string across the gray plain back to the twinkling village lights.

Day after day Mowgli would lead the buffaloes out to their wallows, and day after day he would see Gray Brother's back a mile and a half away across the plain (so he knew that Shere Khan had not come back), and day after day he would lie on the grass listening to the noises round him, and dreaming of old days in the jungle. If Shere Khan had made a false step with his lame paw up in the jungles by the Waingunga, Mowgli would have heard him in those long still mornings.

At last a day came when he did not see Gray Brother at the signal place, and he laughed and headed the buffaloes for the ravine by the *dhâk*-tree, which was all covered with golden-red flowers. There sat Gray Brother, every bristle on his back lifted.

'He has hidden for a month to throw thee off thy guard. He crossed the ranges last night with Tabaqui, hot-foot on thy trail,' said the Wolf, panting.

Mowgli frowned. 'I am not afraid of Shere Khan, but Tabaqui is very cunning.'

'Have no fear,' said Gray Brother, licking his lips a little. 'I met Tabaqui in the dawn. Now he is telling all his wisdom to the kites, but he told *me* everything before I broke his back. Shere Khan's plan is to wait for thee at the village gate this evening—for thee and for no one else. He is lying up now, in the big dry ravine of the Waingunga.'

'Has he eaten to-day, or does he hunt empty?' said Mowgli, for the answer meant life and death to him.

'He killed at dawn—a pig—and he has drunk too. Remember, Shere Khan could never fast, even for the sake of revenge.'

'Oh! fool, fool! What a cub's cub it is! Eaten and drunk too, and he thinks that I shall wait till he has slept! Now, where does he lie up? If there were but ten of us we might pull him down as he lies. These buffaloes will not charge unless they wind him, and I cannot speak their language. Can we get behind his track so that they may smell it?'

'He swam far down the Waingunga to cut that off,' said Gray Brother.

'Tabaqui told him that, I know. He would never have thought of it alone.' Mowgli stood with his finger in his mouth, thinking. 'The big ravine of the Waingunga. That opens out on the plain not half a mile from here. I can take the herd round through the jungle to the head of the ravine and then sweep down—but he would slink out at the foot. We must block that end. Gray Brother, canst thou cut the herd in two for me?'

'Not I, perhaps—but I have brought a wise helper.' Gray Brother trotted off and dropped into a hole. Then there lifted up a huge gray head that Mowgli knew well, and the hot air was filled with the most desolate cry of all the jungle—the hunting-howl of a wolf at mid-day.

'Akela! Akela!' said Mowgli, clapping his hands. 'I might have known that thou wouldst not forget me. We have a big work in hand. Cut the herd in two, Akela. Keep the cows and calves together, and the bulls and the plough-buffaloes by themselves.'

The two wolves ran, ladies'-chain fashion, in and out of the herd, which snorted and threw up its head, and separated into two clumps. In one, the cow-buffaloes stood with their calves in the centre, and glared and pawed, ready, if a wolf would only stay still, to charge down and trample the life out of him. In the other, the bulls and the young bulls snorted and stamped, but though they looked more imposing they were much less dangerous, for they had no calves to protect. No six men could have divided the herd so neatly.

'What orders!' panted Akela. 'They are trying to join again.'

Mowgli slipped on to Rama's back. 'Drive the bulls away to the left, Akela. Gray Brother, when we are gone, hold the cows together, and drive them into the foot of the ravine.'

'How far?' said Gray Brother, panting and snapping.

'Till the sides are higher than Shere Khan can jump,' shouted Mowgli. 'Keep them there till we come down.' The bulls swept off as Akela bayed, and Gray Brother stopped in front of the cows. They charged down on him, and he ran just before them to the foot of the ravine, as Akela drove the bulls far to the left.

'Well done! Another charge and they are fairly started. Careful, now—careful, Akela. A snap too much, and the bulls will charge. *Hujah!* This is wilder work than driving black-buck. Didst thou think these creatures could move so swiftly?' Mowgli called.

'I have—have hunted these too in my time,' gasped Akela in the dust. 'Shall I turn them into the jungle?'

'Ay! Turn. Swiftly turn them! Rama is mad with rage. Oh, if I could only tell him what I need of him to-day.'

The bulls were turned, to the right this time, and crashed into the standing thicket. The other herd-children, watching with the cattle half a mile away, hurried to the village as fast as their legs could carry them, crying that the buffaloes had gone mad and run away. But Mowgli's plan was simple enough. All he wanted to do was to make a big circle uphill and get at the head of the ravine, and then take the bulls down it and catch Shere Khan between the bulls and the cows; for he knew that after a meal and a full drink Shere Khan would not be in any condition to fight or to clamber up the sides of the ravine. He was soothing the buffaloes now by voice and Akela had dropped far to the rear, only whimpering once or twice to hurry the rear-guard. It was a long, long circle, for they did not wish to get too near the ravine and give Shere Khan warning. At last Mowgli rounded up the bewildered herd at the head of the ravine on a grassy patch that sloped steeply down to the ravine itself. From that height you could see across the tops of the trees down to the plain below; but what Mowgli looked at was the sides of the ravine, and he saw with a great deal of satisfaction that they ran nearly straight up and down, while the vines and creepers that hung over them would give no foothold to a tiger who wanted to get out.

'Let them breathe, Akela,' he said, holding up his hand.

'They have not winded him yet. Let them breathe. I must tell Shere Khan who comes. We have him in a trap.'

He put his hands to his mouth and shouted down the ravine,—it was almost like shouting down a tunnel,—and the echoes jumped from rock to rock.

After a long time there came back the drawling, sleepy snarl of a full-fed tiger just wakened.

'Who calls?' said Shere Khan, and a splendid peacock fluttered up out of the ravine screeching.

'I, Mowgli. Cattle thief, it is time to come to the Council Rock! Down—hurry them down, Akela! Down, Rama, down!'

The herd paused for an instant at the edge of the slope, but Akela gave tongue in the full hunting yell, and they pitched over one after the other just as steamers shoot rapids, the sand and stones spurting up round them. Once started, there was no chance of stopping, and before they were fairly in the bed of the ravine Rama winded Shere Khan and bellowed.

'Ha! Ha!' said Mowgli, on his back. 'Now thou knowest!' and the torrent of black horns, foaming muzzles, and staring eyes whirled down the ravine just as boulders go down in flood-time; the weaker buffaloes being shouldered out to the sides of the ravine where they tore through the creepers. They knew what the business was before them —the terrible charge of the buffalo herd against which no tiger can hope to stand. Shere Khan heard the thunder of their hoofs, picked himself up and lumbered down the ravine, looking from side to side for some way of escape, but the walls of the ravine were straight and he had to hold on, heavy with his dinner and drink, willing to do anything rather than fight. The herd splashed through the pool he had just left, bellowing till the narrow cut rang. Mowgli heard an answering bellow from the foot of the ravine, saw Shere Khan turn (the tiger knew if the worst came to the worst it was better to meet the bulls than the cows with their calves), and then Rama tripped, and stumbled, and went on again over something soft, and, with the bulls at his heels, crashed full into the other herd, while the weaker buffaloes were lifted clean off their feet by the shock of the meeting. That charge carried both herds out into the plain, goring and stamping and snorting. Mowgli watched his time, and slipped off Rama's neck, laying about right and left with his stick.

'Quick, Akela! Break them up. Scatter them, or they will be fighting one another. Drive them away, Akela. *Hai*, Rama! *Hai! hai! hai!* my children. Softly now, softly! It is all over.'

Akela and Gray Brother ran to and fro nipping the buffaloes' legs, and though the herd wheeled once to charge up the ravine again, Mowgli managed to turn Rama, and the others followed him to the wallows.

Shere Khan needed no more trampling. He was dead, and the kites were coming for him already.

'Brothers, that was a dog's death,' said Mowgli, feeling for the knife he always carried in a sheath round his neck now that he lived with men. 'But he would never have shown fight. *Wallah!* his hide will look well on the Council Rock. We must get to work swiftly.'

A boy trained among men would never have dreamed of skinning a ten-foot tiger alone, but Mowgli knew better than any one else how an animal's skin is fitted on, and how it can be taken off. But it was hard work, and Mowgli slashed and tore and grunted for an hour, while the wolves lolled out their tongues, or came forward and tugged as he ordered them. Presently a hand fell on his shoulder, and looking up he saw Buldeo with the Tower musket. The children had told the village about the buffalo stampede, and Buldeo went out angrily, only too anxious to correct Mowgli for not taking better care of the herd. The wolves dropped out of sight as soon as they saw the man coming.

'What is this folly?' said Buldeo, angrily. 'To think that thou canst skin a tiger! Where did the buffaloes kill him? It is the Lame Tiger, too, and there is a hundred rupees on his head. Well, well, we will overlook thy letting the herd run off, and perhaps I will give thee one of the rupees of the reward when I have taken the skin to Khanhiwara. He fumbled in his waist-cloth for flint and steel, and stooped down to singe Shere Khan's whiskers. Most native hunters always singe a tiger's whiskers to prevent his ghost from haunting them.

'Hum!' said Mowgli, half to himself as he ripped back the skin of a forepaw. 'So thou wilt take the hide to Khanhiwara for the reward, and perhaps give me one rupee? Now it is in my mind that I need the skin for my own use. Heh! old man, take away that fire!'

'What talk is this to the chief hunter of the village? Thy luck and the stupidity of thy buffaloes have helped thee to this kill. The tiger has just fed, or he would have gone twenty miles by this time. Thou canst not even skin him properly, little beggar brat, and forsooth I, Buldeo, must be told not to singe his whiskers. Mowgli, I will not give thee one anna of the reward, but only a very big beating. Leave the carcass!'

'By the Bull that bought me,' said Mowgli, who was trying to get at the shoulder, 'must I stay babbling to an old ape all noon? Here, Akela, this man plagues me.'

Buldeo, who was still stooping over Shere Khan's head, found himself sprawling on the grass, with a gray wolf standing over him, while Mowgli went on skinning as though he were alone in all India.

'Ye-es,' he said, between his teeth. 'Thou art altogether right, Buldeo. Thou wilt never give me one anna of the reward. There is an old war between this lame tiger and myself—a very old war, and—I have won.'

To do Buldeo justice, if he had been ten years younger he would have taken his chance with Akela had he met the wolf in the woods, but a wolf who obeyed the orders of this boy who had private wars with man-eating tigers was not a common animal. It was sorcery, magic of the worst kind, thought Buldeo, and he wondered whether the amulet round his neck would protect him. He lay as still as still, expecting every minute to see Mowgli turn into a tiger, too.

'Maharaj! Great King,' he said at last, in a husky whisper.

'Yes,' said Mowgli, without turning his head, chuckling a little.

'I am an old man. I did not know that thou wast anything more than a herdsboy. May I rise up and go away, or will thy servant tear me to pieces?'

'Go, and peace go with thee. Only, another time do not meddle with my game. Let him go, Akela.'

Buldeo hobbled away to the village as fast as he could, looking back over his shoulder in case Mowgli should change into something terrible. When he got to the village he told a tale of magic and enchantment and sorcery that made the priest look very grave.

Mowgli went on with his work, but it was nearly twilight before he and the wolves had drawn the great gray skin clear of the body.

'Now we must hide this and take the buffaloes home! Help me to herd them, Akela.'

The herd rounded up in the misty twilight, and when they got near the village Mowgli saw lights, and heard the conches and bells in the temple blowing and banging. Half the village seemed to be waiting for him by the gate. 'That is because I have killed Shere Khan,' he said to himself; but a shower of stones whistled about his ears, and the villagers shouted: 'Sorcerer! Wolf's brat! Jungle-demon! Go away! Get hence quickly, or the priest will turn thee into a wolf again. Shoot, Buldeo, shoot!'

The old Tower musket went off with a bang, and a young buffalo bellowed in pain.

'More sorcery!' shouted the villagers. 'He can turn bullets. Buldeo, that was *thy* buffalo.'

'Now what is this?' said Mowgli, bewildered, as the stones flew thicker.

'They are not unlike the Pack, these brothers of thine,' said Akela, sitting down composedly. 'It is in my head that, if bullets mean anything, they would cast thee out.'

'Wolf! Wolf's cub! Go away!' shouted the priest, waving a sprig of the sacred *tulsi* plant.

'Again? Last time it was because I was a man. This time it is because I am a wolf. Let us go, Akela.'

A woman—it was Messua—ran across to the herd, and cried: 'Oh, my son, my son! They say thou art a sorcerer who can turn himself into a beast at will. I do not believe, but go away or they will kill thee. Buldeo says thou art a wizard, but I know thou hast avenged Nathoo's death.'

'Come back, Messua!' shouted the crowd. 'Come back, or we will stone thee.'

Mowgli laughed a little short ugly laugh, for a stone had hit him in the mouth. 'Run back, Messua. This is one of the foolish tales they tell under the big tree at dusk. I have at least paid for thy son's life. Farewell; and run quickly, for I shall send the herd in more swiftly than their brick-bats. I am no wizard, Messua. Farewell!'

'Now, once more, Akela,' he cried. 'Bring the herd in.'

The buffaloes were anxious enough to get to the village. They hardly needed Akela's yell, but charged through the gate like a whirlwind, scattering the crowd right and left.

'Keep count!' shouted Mowgli, scornfully. 'It may be that I have stolen one of them. Keep count, for I will do your herding no more. Fare you well, children of men, and thank Messua that I do not come in with my wolves and hunt you up and down your street.'

He turned on his heel and walked away with the Lone Wolf; and as he looked up at the stars he felt happy. 'No more sleeping in traps for me, Akela. Let us get Shere Khan's skin and go away. No; we will not hurt the village, for Messua was kind to me.'

When the moon rose over the plain, making it look all milky, the horrified villagers saw Mowgli, with two wolves at his heels and a bundle on his head, trotting across at the steady wolf's trot that eats up the long miles like fire. Then they banged the temple bells and blew the conches louder than ever; and Messua cried, and Buldeo embroidered the story of his adventures in the jungle, till he ended by saying that Akela stood up on his hind legs and talked like a man.

The moon was just going down when Mowgli and the two wolves came to the hill of the Council Rock, and they stopped at Mother Wolf's cave.

'They have cast me out from the man Pack, Mother,' shouted Mowgli, 'but I come with the hide of Shere Khan to keep my word.' Mother Wolf walked stiffly from the cave with the cubs behind her, and her eyes glowed as she saw the skin.

'I told him on that day, when he crammed his head and shoulders into this cave, hunting for thy life, little frog—I told him that the hunter would be the hunted. It is well done.'

'Little Brother, it is well done,' said a deep voice in the thicket. 'We were lonely in the jungle without thee,' and Bagheera came running to Mowgli's bare feet. They clambered up the Council Rock together, and Mowgli spread the skin out on the flat stone where Akela used to sit, and pegged it down with four slivers of bamboo, and

Akela lay down upon it, and called the old call to the Council, 'Look, look well, O Wolves,' exactly as he had called when Mowgli was first brought there.

Ever since Akela had been deposed, the Pack had been without a leader, hunting and fighting at their own pleasure. But they answered the call from habit; and some of them were lame from the traps they had fallen into, and some limped from shot-wounds, and some were mangy from eating bad food, and many were missing; but they came to the Council Rock, all that were left of them, and saw Shere Khan's striped hide on the rock, and the huge claws dangling at the end of the empty dangling feet.

'Look well, O Wolves. Have I kept my word?' said Mowgli; and the wolves bayed Yes, and one tattered wolf howled:—

'Lead us again, O Akela. Lead us again, O man-cub, for we be sick of this lawlessness, and we would be the Free People once more.'

'Nay,' purred Bagheera, 'that may not be. When ye are full fed, the madness may come upon you again. Not for nothing are ye called the Free People. Ye fought for freedom, and it is yours. Eat it, O Wolves.'

'Man-Pack and Wolf-Pack have cast me out,' said Mowgli. 'Now I will hunt alone in the jungle.'

'And we will hunt with thee,' said the four cubs.

So Mowgli went away and hunted with the four cubs in the jungle from that day on. But he was not always alone, because, years afterward, he became a man and married.

But that is a story for grown-ups.

MOWGLI'S SONG

THAT HE SANG AT THE COUNCIL ROCK WHEN HE DANCED ON SHERE KHAN'S HIDE.

THE Song of Mowgli—I, Mowgli am singing. Let the jungle listen to the things I have done.

Shere Khan said he would kill—would kill! At the gates in the twilight he would kill Mowgli, the Frog!

He ate and he drank. Drink deep, Shere Khan, for when wilt thou drink again? Sleep and dream of the kill.

I am alone on the grazing-grounds. Gray Brother come to me! Come to me, Lone Wolf, for there is big game afoot!

Bring up the great bull-buffaloes, the blue-skinned herd-bulls with the angry eyes. Drive them to and fro as I order. Sleepest thou still, Shere Khan? Wake, O wake! Here come I, and the bulls are behind.

Rama the king of the buffaloes stamped with his foot. Waters of the Waingunga whither went Shere Khan?

He is not Sahi to dig holes, nor Mor, the Peacock, that he should fly. He is not Mang, the Bat, to hang in the branches. Little bamboos that creak together tell me where he ran?

Ow! he is there. *Ahoo!* he is there. Under the feet of Rama lies the Lame One! Up, Shere Khan! Up and kill! Here is meat; break the necks of the bulls.

Hsh! he is asleep. We will not wake him, for his strength is very great. The kites have come down to see it. The black ants have come up to know it. There is a great assembly in his honour.

Alala! I have no cloth to wrap me. The kites will see that I am naked. I am ashamed to meet all these people.

Lend me thy coat, Shere Khan. Lend me thy gay striped coat that I may go to the Council Rock.

By the Bull that bought me I made a promise—a little promise. Only thy coat is lacking before I keep my word.

With the knife, with the knife that men use, with the knife of the hunter, I will stoop down for my gift.

Waters of the Waingunga, Shere Khan gives me his coat for the love that he bears me. Pull, Gray Brother!

Pull, Akela! Heavy is the hide of Shere Khan.

The Man Pack are angry. They throw stones and talk child's talk. My mouth is bleeding. Let me run away.

Through the night, through the hot night, run swiftly with me, my brothers. We will leave the lights of the village and go to the low moon.

Waters of the Waingunga, the Man Pack have cast me out. I did them no harm, but they were afraid of me. Why?

Wolf Pack, ye have cast me out too. The Jungle is shut to me and the village gates are shut. Why?

As Mang flies between the beasts and birds so fly I between the village and the Jungle. Why?

I dance on the hide of Shere Khan, but my heart is very heavy. My mouth is cut and wounded with the stones from the village, but my heart is very light, because I have come back to the Jungle. Why?

These two things fight together in me as the snakes fight in the spring. The water comes out of my eyes; yet I laugh while it falls. Why?

I am two Mowglis, but the hide of Shere Khan is under my feet.

All the Jungle knows that I have killed Shere Khan. Look, look well, O Wolves!

Ahae! my heart is heavy with the things that I do not understand.

TODS' AMENDMENT.

The World hath set its heavy yoke
Upon the old white-bearded folk
  Who strive to please the King.
God's mercy is upon the young,
God's wisdom in the baby tongue
  That fears not anything.

The Parable of Chajju Bhagat.

NOW Tods' Mamma was a singularly charming woman, and every one in Simla knew Tods. Most men had saved him from death on occasions. He was beyond his *ayah's* control altogether, and perilled his life daily to find out what would happen if you pulled a Mountain Battery mule's tail. He was an utterly fearless young Pagan, about six years old, and the only baby who ever broke the holy calm of the Supreme Legislative Council.

It happened this way: Tods' pet kid got loose, and fled up the hill, off the Boileaugunge Road, Tods after it, until it burst in to the Viceregal Lodge lawn, then attached to 'Peterhoff.' The Council were sitting at the time, and the windows were open because it was warm. The Red Lancer in the porch told Tods to go away; but Tods knew the Red Lancer and most of the Members of Council personally. Moreover, he had firm hold of the kid's collar, and was being dragged all across the flower-beds. 'Give my *salaam* to the long Councillor *Sahib*, and ask him to help me take *Moti* back!' gasped Tods. The Council heard the noise through the open windows; and, after an interval, was seen the shocking spectacle of a Legal Member and a Lieutenant-Governor helping, under the direct patronage of a Commander-in-Chief and a Viceroy, one small and very dirty boy, in a sailor's suit and a tangle of brown hair, to coerce a lively and rebellious kid. They headed it off down the path to the Mall, and Tods went home in triumph and told his Mamma that *all* the Councillor *Sahibs* had been helping him to catch *Moti.* Whereat his Mamma smacked Tods for interfering with the administration of the Empire; but Tods met the Legal Member the next day, and told him in confidence that if the Legal Member ever wanted to catch a goat, he, Tods, would give him all the help in his power. 'Thank you, Tods,' said the Legal Member.

Tods was the idol of some eighty *jhampanis*, and half as many *saises*. He saluted them all as 'O Brother.' It never entered his head that any living human being could disobey his orders; and he was the buffer between the servants and his Mamma's wrath. The working of that household turned on Tods, who was adored by every one from the *dhoby* to the dog-boy. Even Futteh Khan, the villainous loafer *khit* from Mussoorie, shirked risking Tods' displeasure for fear his co-mates should look down on him.

So Tods had honour in the land from Boileaugunge to Chota Simla, and ruled justly according to his lights. Of course, he spoke Urdu, but he had also mastered many queer side-speeches like the *chotee bolee* of the women, and held grave converse with shopkeepers and Hill-coolies alike. He was precocious for his age, and his mixing with natives had taught him some of the more bitter truths of life: the meanness and the sordidness of it. He used, over his bread and milk, to deliver solemn and serious aphorisms, translated from the vernacular into the English, that made his Mamma jump and vow that Tods *must* go Home next hot weather.

Just when Tods was in the bloom of his power, the

Supreme Legislature were hacking out a Bill for the Sub-Montane Tracts, a revision of the then Act, smaller than the Punjab Land Bill, but affecting a few hundred thousand people none the less. The Legal Member had built, and bolstered, and embroidered, and amended that Bill till it looked beautiful on paper. Then the Council began to settle what they called the 'minor details.' As if any Englishman legislating for natives knows enough to know which are the minor and which are the major points, from the native point of view, of any measure! That Bill was a triumph of 'safe-guarding the interests of the tenant.' One clause provided that land should not be leased on longer terms than five years at a stretch; because, if the landlord had a tenant bound down for, say, twenty years, he would squeeze the very life out of him. The notion was to keep up a stream of independent cultivators in the Sub-Montane Tracts; and ethnologically and politically the notion was correct. The only drawback was that it was altogether wrong. A native's life in India implies the life of his son. Wherefore, you cannot legislate for one generation at a time. You must consider the next from the native point of view. Curiously enough, the native now and then, and in Northern India more particularly, hates being over-protected against himself. There was a Naga Village once, where they lived on dead *and* buried Commissariat mules. . . . But that is another story.

For many reasons, to be explained later, the people concerned objected to the Bill. The Native Member in Council knew as much about Punjabis as he knew about Charing Cross. He had said in Calcutta that 'the Bill was entirely in accord with the desires of that large and important class, the cultivators'; and so on, and so on. The Legal Member's knowledge of natives was limited to English-speaking Durbaris, and his own red *chaprassis*, the Sub-Montane Tracts concerned no one in particular, the

Deputy Commissioners were a good deal too driven to make representations, and the measure was one which dealt with small land-holders only. Nevertheless, the Legal Member prayed that it might be correct, for he was a nervously conscientious man. He did not know that no man can tell what natives think unless he mixes with them with the varnish off. And not always then. But he did the best he knew. And the measure came up to the Supreme Council for the final touches, while Tods patrolled the Burra Simla Bazar in his morning rides, and played with the monkey belonging to Ditta Mull, the *bunnia*, and listened, as a child listens, to all the stray talk about this new freak of the *Lord Sahib's*.

One day there was a dinner-party at the house of Tods' Mamma, and the Legal Member came. Tods was in bed, but he kept awake till he heard the bursts of laughter from the men over the coffee. Then he paddled out in his little red flannel dressing-gown and his night-suit, and took refuge by the side of his father, knowing that he would not be sent back. 'See the miseries of having a family!' said Tods' father, giving Tods three prunes, some water in a glass that had been used for claret, and telling him to sit still. Tods sucked the prunes slowly, knowing that he would have to go when they were finished, and sipped the pink water like a man of the world, as he listened to the conversation. Presently, the Legal Member, talking 'shop' to the Head of a Department, mentioned his Bill by its full name—'The Sub-Montane Tracts *Ryotwary* Revised Enactment.' Tods caught the one native word, and lifting up his small voice said—

'Oh, I know *all* about that! Has it been *murramutted* yet, Councillor *Sahib*?'

'How much?' said the Legal Member.

'*Murramutted*—mended.—Put *theek*, you know—made nice to please Ditta Mull!'

The Legal Member left his place and moved up next to Tods.

'What do you know about *ryotwari*, little man?' he said.

'I'm not a little man, I'm Tods, and I know *all* about it. Ditta Mull, and Choga Lall, and Amir Nath, and—oh, *lakhs* of my friends tell me about it in the bazars when I talk to them.'

'Oh, they do—do they? What do they say, Tods?'

Tods tucked his feet under his red flannel dressing-gown and said—'I must *fink*.'

The Legal Member waited patiently. Then Tods, with infinite compassion—

'You don't speak my talk, do you, Councillor *Sahib*?'

'No; I am sorry to say I do not,' said the Legal Member.

'Very well,' said Tods, 'I must *fink* in English.'

He spent a minute putting his ideas in order, and began very slowly, translating in his mind from the vernacular to English, as many Anglo-Indian children do. You must remember that the Legal Member helped him on by questions when he halted. for Tods was not equal to the sustained flight of oratory that follows.

'Ditta Mull says, "This thing is the talk of a child, and was made up by fools." But *I* don't think you are a fool, Councillor *Sahib*,' said Tods hastily. 'You caught my goat. This is what Ditta Mull says—"I am not a fool, and why should the Sirkar say I am a child? I can see if the land is good and if the landlord is good. If I am a fool, the sin is upon my own head. For five years I take my ground for which I have saved money, and a wife I take too, and a little son is born." Ditta Mull has one daughter now, but he *says* he will have a son soon. And he says, "At the end of five years, by this new *bundobust*, I must go. If I do not go, I must get fresh seals and *takkus*-stamps on the papers, perhaps in the middle of the harvest, and to go to the law-courts once is wisdom, but to go twice is *Jehannum*." 'That is *quite* true,' explained Tods gravely. 'All my friends say so. And Ditta Mull says, "Always fresh *takkus* and paying money to *vakils* and *chaprassis* and law-courts every five years, or else the landlord makes me go. Why do I want to go? Am I a fool? If I am a fool and do not know, after forty years, good land when I see it, let me die! But if the new *bundobust* says for *fifteen* years, that is good and wise. My little son is a man, and I am burnt, and he takes the ground or another ground, paying only once for the *takkus*-stamps on the papers, and his little son is born, and at the end of fifteen years is a man too. But what profit is there in five years and fresh papers? Nothing but *dikh*, trouble, *dikh*. We are not young men who take these lands, but old ones—not farmers, but tradesmen with a little money—and for fifteen years we shall have peace. Nor are we children that the Sirkar should treat us so."'

Here Tods stopped short, for the whole table were listening. The Legal Member said to Tods, 'Is that all?'

'All I can remember,' said Tods. 'But you should see Ditta Mull's big monkey. It's just like a Councillor *Sahib*.'

'Tods! Go to bed!' said his father.

Tods gathered up his dressing-gown tail and departed.

The Legal Member brought his hand down on the table with a crash—'By Jove!' said the Legal Member, 'I believe the boy is right. The short tenure *is* the weak point.'

He left early, thinking over what Tods had said. Now, it was obviously impossible for the Legal Member to play with a *bunnia's* monkey, by way of getting understanding; but he did better. He made inquiries, always bearing in mind the fact that the real native—not the hybrid, University-trained mule—is as timid as a colt, and little by little, he coaxed some of the men whom the measure concerned most intimately to give in their views, which squared very closely with Tods' evidence.

So the Bill was amended in that clause; and the Legal Member was filled with an uneasy suspicion that Native Members represent very little except the Orders they carry on their bosoms. But he put the thought from him as illiberal. He was a most liberal man.

After a time the news spread through the bazars that Tods had got the Bill recast in the tenure-clause, and, if Tods' Mamma had not interfered, Tods would have made himself sick on the baskets of fruit and pistachio nuts and Cabuli grapes and almonds that crowded the verandah. Till he went Home, Tods ranked some few degrees before the Viceroy in popular estimation. But for the little life of him Tods could not understand why.

In the Legal Member's private-paper-box still lies the rough draft of the Sub-Montane Tracts *Ryotwary* Revised Enactment; and opposite the twenty-second clause, pencilled in blue chalk, and signed by the Legal Member are the words '*Tods' Amendment.*'

THE STORY OF MUHAMMAD DIN

Who is the happy man? He that sees in his own house, at home, little children crowned with dust, leaping and falling and crying.—*Munichandra*, translated by Professor Peterson.

THE polo-ball was an old one, scarred, chipped, and dinted. It stood on the mantelpiece among the pipe-stems which Imam Din, *khitmatgar*, was cleaning for me.

'Does the Heaven-born want this ball?' said Imam Din deferentially.

The Heaven-born set no particular store by it; but of what use was a polo ball to a *khitmatgar*?

'By Your Honour's favour, I have a little son. He has seen this ball, and desires it to play with, I do not want it for myself.'

No one would for an instant accuse portly old Imam Din of wanting to play with polo-balls. He carried out the battered thing into the verandah; and there followed a hurricane of joyful squeaks, a patter of small feet, and the *thud-thud-thud* of the ball rolling along the ground. Evidently the little son had been waiting outside the door to secure his treasure. But how had he managed to see that polo-ball?

Next day, coming back from office half an hour earlier than usual, I was aware of a small figure in the dining-room—a tiny, plump figure in a ridiculously inadequate shirt which came, perhaps, halfway down the tubby stomach. It wandered round the room, thumb in mouth, crooning to itself as it took stock of the pictures. Undoubtedly this was the 'little son.'

He had no business in my room, of course; but was so deeply absorbed in his discoveries that he never noticed me in the doorway. I stepped into the room and startled him nearly into a fit. He sat down on the ground with a gasp. His eyes opened, and his mouth followed suit. I knew what was coming, and fled, followed by a long, dry howl which reached the servants' quarters far more quickly than any command of mine had ever done. In ten seconds Imam Din was in the dining-room. Then despairing sobs arose, and I returned to find Imam Din admonishing the small sinner who was using most of his shirt as a handkerchief.

'This boy,' said Imam Din judicially, 'is a *budmash*—a big *budmash*. He will, without doubt, go to the *jail-khana* for his behaviour.' Renewed yells from the penitent, and an elaborate apology to myself from Imam Din.

'Tell the baby,' said I, 'that the *Sahib* is not angry, and take him away.' Imam Din conveyed my forgiveness to the offender, who had now gathered all his shirt round his neck, stringwise, and the yell subsided into a sob. The two set off for the door. 'His name,' said Imam Din, as though the name were part of the crime, 'is Muhammad Din, and he is a *budmash*.' Freed from present danger, Muhammad Din turned round in his father's arms, and said gravely, 'It is true that my name is Muhammad Din, *Tahib*, but I am not a *budmash*. I am a *man!*'

From that day dated my acquaintance with Muhammad Din. Never again did he come into my dining-room, but on the neutral ground of the garden we greeted each other with much state, though our conversation was confined to '*Talaam, Tahib*' from his side, and '*Salaam, Muhammad Din*' from mine. Daily on my return from office, the little white shirt and the fat little body used to rise from the shade of the creeper-covered trellis where they had been hid; and daily I checked my horse here, that my salutation might not be slurred over or given unseemly.

Muhammad Din never had any companions. He used to trot about the compound, in and out of the castor-oil bushes, on mysterious errands of his own. One day I stumbled upon some of his handiwork far down the grounds. He had half buried the polo-ball in dust, and stuck six shrivelled old marigold flowers in a circle round it. Outside that circle again was a rude square, traced out in bits of red brick alternating with fragments of broken china; the whole bounded by a little bank of dust. The water-man from the well-curb put in a plea for the small architect, saying that it was only the play of a baby and did not much disfigure my garden.

Heaven knows that I had no intention of touching the child's work then or later; but, that evening, a stroll through the garden brought me unawares full on it; so that I trampled, before I knew, marigold-heads, dust-bank, and fragments of broken soap dish into confusion past all hope of mending. Next morning, I came upon Muhammad Din crying softly to himself over the ruin I had wrought. Some one had cruelly told him that the *Sahib* was very angry with him for spoiling the garden, and had scattered his rubbish, using bad language the while. Muhammad Din laboured for an hour at effacing every trace of the dust bank and pottery fragments, and it was with a tearful and apologetic face that he said, '*Talaam, Tahib*,' when I came home from office. A hasty inquiry resulted in Imam Din informing Muhammad Din that, by my singular favour, he was permitted to disport himself as he pleased. Whereat the child took heart and fell to tracing the ground-plan of an edifice which was to eclipse the marigold-polo-ball creation.

For some months the chubby little eccentricity revolved in his humble orbit among the castor-oil bushes and in the dust; always fashioning magnificent palaces from stale flowers thrown away by the bearer, smooth water-worn pebbles, bits of broken glass, and feathers pulled, I fancy, from my fowls—always alone, and always crooning to himself.

A gaily-spotted sea-shell was dropped one day close to the last of his little buildings; and I looked that Muhammad Din should build something more than ordinarily splendid on the strength of it. Nor was I disappointed. He meditated for the better part of an hour, and his crooning rose to a jubilant song. Then he began tracing in the dust. It would certainly be a wondrous palace, this one, for it was two yards long and a yard broad in ground-plan. But the palace was never completed.

Next day there was no Muhammad Din at the head of the carriage-drive, and no '*Talaam, Tahib*' to welcome my return. I had grown accustomed to the greeting, and its omission troubled me. Next day Imam Din told me that the child was suffering slightly from fever and needed quinine. He got the medicine, and an English Doctor.

'They have no stamina, these brats,' said the Doctor, as he left Imam Din's quarters.

A week later, though I would have given much to have avoided it, I met on the road to the Mussulman burying-ground Imam Din, accompanied by one other friend, carrying in his arms, wrapped in a white cloth, all that was left of little Muhammad Din.

THE FINANCES OF THE GODS

THE evening meal was ended in Dhunni Bhagat's Chubara, and the old priests were smoking or counting their beads. A little naked child pattered in, with its mouth wide open, a handful of marigold flowers in one hand, and a lump of conserved tobacco in the other. It tried to kneel and make obeisance to Gobind, but it was so fat that it fell forward on its shaven head, and rolled on its side, kicking and gasping, while the marigolds tumbled one way and the tobacco the other. Gobind laughed, set it up again, and blessed the marigold flowers as he received the tobacco.

'From my father,' said the child. 'He has the fever, and cannot come. Wilt thou pray for him, father?'

'Surely, littlest; but the smoke is on the ground, and the night-chill is in the air, and it is not good to go abroad naked in the autumn.'

'I have no clothes,' said the child, 'and all to-day I have been carrying cow-dung cakes to the bazar. It was very hot, and I am very tired.' It shivered a little, for the twilight was cool.

Gobind lifted an arm under his vast tattered quilt of many colours, and made an inviting little nest by his side. The child crept in, and Gobind filled his brass-studded leather waterpipe with the new tobacco. When I came to the Chubara the shaven head with the tuft atop, and the beady black eyes looked out of the folds of the quilt as a squirrel looks out from his nest, and Gobind was smiling while the child played with his beard.

I would have said something friendly, but remembered in time that if the child fell ill afterwards I should be credited with the Evil Eye, and that is a horrible possession.

'Sit thou still, Thumbling,' I said, as it made to get up and run away. 'Where is thy slate, and why has the teacher let such an evil character loose on the streets when there are no police to protect us weaklings? In which ward dost thou try to break thy neck with flying kites from the house-top?'

'Nay, Sahib, nay,' said the child, burrowing its face into Gobind's beard, and twisting uneasily. 'There was a holiday to-day among the schools, and I do not always fly kites. I play ker-li-kit like the rest.'

Cricket is the national game among the school-boys of the Punjab, from the naked hedge-school children, who use an old kerosine-tin for wicket, to the B.A.'s of the University, who compete for the Championship belt.

'Thou play kerlikit! Thou art half the weight of the bat!' I said.

The child nodded resolutely. 'Yea, I *do* play. *Perlay-ball. Ow-at! Ran, ran, ran!* I know it all.'

'But thou must not forget with all this to pray to the Gods according to custom,' said Gobind, who did not altogether approve of cricket and Western innovations.

'I do not forget,' said the child in a hushed voice.

'Also to give reverence to thy teacher, and'—Gobind's voice softened—'to abstain from pulling holy men by the beard, little badling. Eh, eh, eh?'

The child's face was altogether hidden in the great white beard, and it began to whimper till Gobind soothed it as children are soothed all the world over, with the promise of a story.

'I did not think to frighten thee, senseless little one.

Look up! Am I angry? Aré, aré, aré! Shall I weep too, and of our tears make a great pond and drown us both, and then thy father will never get well, lacking thee to pull his beard? Peace, peace, and I will tell thee of the Gods. Thou hast heard many tales?'

'Very many, father.'

'Now, this is a new one, which thou hast not heard. Long and long ago when the Gods walked with men, as they do to-day, but that we have not faith to see, Shiv, the greatest of Gods, and Parbati his wife, were walking in the garden of a temple.'

'Which temple? That in the Nandgaon ward?' said the child.

'Nay, very far away. Maybe at Trimbak or Hurdwar, whither thou must make pilgrimage when thou art a man. Now, there was sitting in the garden under the jujube trees, a mendicant that had worshipped Shiv for forty years, and he lived on the offerings of the pious, and meditated holiness night and day.'

'Oh, father, was it thou?' said the child, looking up with large eyes.

'Nay, I have said it was long ago, and, moreover, this mendicant was married.'

'Did they put him on a horse with flowers on his head, and forbid him to go to sleep all night long? Thus they did to me when they made my wedding,' said the child, who had been married a few months before.

'And what didst thou do?' said I.

'I wept, and they called me evil names, and then I smote *her*, and we wept together.'

'Thus did not the mendicant,' said Gobind; 'for he was a holy man, and very poor. Parbati perceived him sitting naked by the temple steps where all went up and down, and she said to Shiv, "What shall men think of the Gods when the Gods thus scorn the worshippers? For forty years yonder man has prayed to us, and yet there be only a few grains of rice and some broken cowries before him after all. Men's hearts will be hardened by this thing." And Shiv said, "It shall be looked to," and so he called to the temple, which was the temple of his son, Ganesh of the elephant head, saying, "Son, there is a mendicant without who is very poor. What wilt thou do for him?" Then that great elephant-headed One awoke in the dark and answered, "In three days, if it be thy will, he shall have one lakh of rupees." Then Shiv and Parbati went away.'

'But there was a money-lender in the garden hidden among the marigolds'—the child looked at the ball of crumpled blossoms in its hands—'ay, among the yellow marigolds, and he heard the Gods talking. He was a covetous man, and of a black heart, and he desired that lakh of rupees for himself. So he went to the mendicant and said, "Oh brother, how much do the pious give thee daily?" The mendicant said, "I cannot tell. Sometimes a little rice, sometimes a little pulse, and a few cowries and, it has been, pickled mangoes, and dried fish."

'That is good,' said the child, smacking its lips.

'Then said the money-lender, "Because I have long watched thee, and learned to love thee and thy patience, I will give thee now five rupees for all thy earnings of the three days to come. There is only a bond to sign on the matter." But the mendicant said, "Thou art mad. In two months I do not receive the worth of five rupees," and he told the thing to his wife that evening. She, being a woman, said, "When did money-lender ever make a bad bargain? The wolf runs the corn for the sake of the fat deer. Our fate is in the hands of the Gods. Pledge it not even for three days."

'So the mendicant returned to the money-lender, and would not sell. Then that wicked man sat all day before him offering more and more for those three days' earnings.

First, ten, fifty, and a hundred rupees; and then, for he did not know when the Gods would pour down their gifts, rupees by the thousand, till he had offered half a lakh of rupees. Upon this sum the mendicant's wife shifted her counsel, and the mendicant signed the bond, and the money was paid in silver; great white bullocks bringing it by the cartload. But saving only all that money, the mendicant received nothing from the Gods at all, and the heart of the money-lender was uneasy on account of expectation. Therefore at noon of the third day the money-lender went into the temple to spy upon the councils of the Gods, and to learn in what manner that gift might arrive. Even as he was making his prayers, a crack between the stones of the floor gaped, and, closing, caught him by the heel. Then he heard the Gods walking in the temple in the darkness of the columns, and Shiv called to his son Ganesh, saying ' Son, what hast thou done in regard to the lakh of rupees for the mendicant?" And Ganesh woke, for the money-lender heard the dry rustle of his trunk uncoiling, and he answered, "Father, one-half of the money has been paid, and the debtor for the other half I hold here fast by the heel."'

The child bubbled with laughter. 'And the money-lender paid the mendicant?' it said.

'Surely, for he whom the Gods hold by the heel must pay to the uttermost. The money was paid at evening, all silver, in great carts, and thus Ganesh did his work.'

'Nathu! Ohē Nathu!'

A woman was calling in the dusk by the door of the courtyard.

The child began to wriggle. 'That is my mother,' it said.

'Go then, littlest,' answered Gobind; 'but stay a moment.'

He ripped a generous yard from his patchwork-quilt, put it over the child's shoulders, and the child ran away.

MOTI GUJ—MUTINEER

ONCE upon a time there was a coffee-planter in India who wished to clear some forest land for coffee-planting. When he had cut down all the trees and burned the under-wood the stumps still remained. Dynamite is expensive and slow-fire slow. The happy medium for stump-clearing is the lord of all beasts, who is the elephant. He will either push the stump out of the ground with his tusks, if he has any, or drag it out with ropes. The planter, therefore, hired elephants by ones and twos and threes, and fell to work. The very best of all the elephants belonged to the very worst of all the drivers or mahouts; and the superior beast's name was Moti Guj. He was the absolute property of his mahout, which would never have been the case under native rule, for Moti Guj was a creature to be desired by kings; and his name, being translated, meant the Pearl Elephant. Because the British Government was in the land, Deesa, the mahout, enjoyed his property undisturbed. He was dissipated. When he had made much money through the strength of his elephant, he would get extremely drunk and give Moti Guj a beating with a tent-peg over the tender nails of the forefeet. Moti Guj never trampled the life out of Deesa on these occasions, for he knew that after the beating was over Deesa would embrace his trunk, and weep and call him his love and his life and the liver of his soul, and give him some liquor. Moti Guj was very fond of liquor—arrack for choice, though he would drink palm-tree toddy if nothing better offered. Then

Deesa would go to sleep between Moti Guj's forefeet, and as Deesa generally chose the middle of the public road, and as Moti Guj mounted guard over him and would not permit horse, foot, or cart to pass by, traffic was congested till Deesa saw fit to wake up.

There was no sleeping in the daytime on the planter's clearing; the wages were too high to risk. Deesa sat on Moti Guj's neck and gave him orders, while Moti Guj rooted up the stumps—for he owned a magnificent pair of tusks; or pulled at the end of a rope—for he had a magnificent pair of shoulders, while Deesa kicked him behind the ears and said he was the king of elephants. At evening time Moti Guj would wash down his three hundred pounds' weight of green food with a quart of arrack, and Deesa would take a share and sing songs between Moti Guj's legs till it was time to go to bed. Once a week Deesa led Moti Guj down to the river, and Moti Guj lay on his side luxuriously in the shallows, while Deesa went over him with a coir-swab and a brick. Moti Guj never mistook the pounding blow of the latter for the smack of the former that warned him to get up and turn over on the other side. Then Deesa would look at his feet, and examine his eyes, and turn up the fringes of his mighty ears in case of sores or budding ophthalmia. After inspection, the two would 'come up with a song from the sea,' Moti Guj all black and shining, waving a torn tree branch twelve feet long in his trunk, and Deesa knotting up his own long wet hair.

It was a peaceful, well-paid life till Deesa felt the return of the desire to drink deep. He wished for an orgie. The little draughts that led nowhere were taking the manhood out of him.

He went to the planter, and 'My mother's dead,' said he, weeping.

'She died on the last plantation two months ago; and she died once before that when you were working for me last year,' said the planter, who knew something of the ways of nativedom.

'Then it's my aunt, and she was just the same as a mother to me,' said Deesa, weeping more than ever. 'She has left eighteen small children entirely without bread, and it is I who must fill their little stomachs,' said Deesa, beating his head on the floor.

'Who brought you the news?' said the planter.

'The post,' said Deesa.

'There hasn't been a post here for the past week. Get back to your lines!'

'A devastating sickness has fallen on my village, and all my wives are dying,' yelled Deesa, really in tears this time.

'Call Chihun, who comes from Deesa's village,' said the planter. 'Chihun, has this man a wife?'

'He!' said Chihun. 'No. Not a woman of our village would look at him. They'd sooner marry the elephant.' Chihun snorted. Deesa wept and bellowed.

'You will get into a difficulty in a minute,' said the planter. 'Go back to your work!'

'Now I will speak Heaven's truth,' gulped Deesa, with an inspiration. 'I haven't been drunk for two months. I desire to depart in order to get properly drunk afar off and distant from this heavenly plantation. Thus I shall cause no trouble.'

A flickering smile crossed the planter's face. 'Deesa,' said he, 'you've spoken the truth, and I'd give you leave on the spot if anything could be done with Moti Guj while you're away. You know that he will only obey your orders.'

'May the Light of the Heavens live forty thousand years. I shall be absent but ten little days. After that, upon my faith and honour and soul, I return. As to the inconsiderable interval, have I the gracious permission of the Heaven-born to call up Moti Guj?'

Permission was granted, and, in answer to Deesa's shrill

yell, the lordly tusker swung out of the shade of a clump of trees where he had been squirting dust over himself till his master should return.

'Light of my heart, Protector of the Drunken, Mountain of Might, give ear,' said Deesa, standing in front of him.

Moti Guj gave ear, and saluted with his trunk, 'I am going away,' said Deesa.

Moti Guj's eyes twinkled. He liked jaunts as well as his master. One could snatch all manner of nice things from the roadside then.

'But you, you fubsy old pig, must stay behind and work.'

The twinkle died out as Moti Guj tried to look delighted. He hated stump-hauling on the plantation. It hurt his teeth.

'I shall be gone for ten days, oh Delectable One. Hold up your near forefoot and I'll impress the fact upon it, warty toad of a dried mud-puddle.' Deesa took a tent-peg and banged Moti Guj ten times on the nails. Moti Guj grunted and shuffled from foot to foot.

'Ten days,' said Deesa, 'you must work and haul and root trees as Chihun here shall order you. Take up Chihun and set him on your neck!' Moti Guj curled the tip of his trunk, Chihun put his foot there and was swung on to the neck. Deesa handed Chihun the heavy *ankus*, the iron elephant-goad.

Chihun thumped Moti Guj's bald head as a paviour thumps a kerbstone.

Moti Guj trumpeted.

'Be still, hog of the backwoods. Chihun's your mahout for ten days. And now bid me good-bye, beast after mine own heart. Oh, my lord, my king! Jewel of all created elephants, lily of the herd, preserve your honoured health; be virtuous. Adieu!'

Moti Guj lapped his trunk round Deesa and swung him into the air twice. That was his way of bidding the man good-bye.

'He'll work now,' said Deesa to the planter. 'Have I leave to go?'

The planter nodded, and Deesa dived into the woods. Moti Guj went back to haul stumps.

Chihun was very kind to him, but he felt unhappy and forlorn notwithstanding. Chihun gave him balls of spices, and tickled him under the chin, and Chihun's little baby cooed to him after work was over, and Chihun's wife called him a darling; but Moti Guj was a bachelor by instinct, as Deesa was. He did not understand the domestic emotions. He wanted the light of his universe back again—the drink and the drunken slumber, the savage beatings and the savage caresses.

None the less he worked well, and the planter wondered. Deesa had vagabonded along the roads till he met a marriage procession of his own caste and, drinking, dancing, and tippling, had drifted past all knowledge of the lapse of time.

The morning of the eleventh day dawned, and there returned no Deesa. Moti Guj was loosed from his ropes for the daily stint. He swung clear, looked round, shrugged his shoulders, and began to walk away, as one having business elsewhere.

'Hi! ho! Come back you,' shouted Chihun. 'Come back, and put me on your neck, Misborn Mountain. Return, Splendour of the Hillsides. Adornment of all India, heave to, or I'll bang every toe off your fat forefoot!'

Moti Guj gurgled gently, but did not obey. Chihun ran after him with a rope and caught him up. Moti Guj put his ears forward, and Chihun knew what that meant, though he tried to carry it off with high words.

'None of your nonsense with me,' said he. 'To your pickets, Devil-son.'

'Hrrump!' said Moti Guj, and that was all—that and the forebent ears.

Moti Guj put his hands in his pockets, chewed a branch for a toothpick, and strolled about the clearing, making jest of the other elephants, who had just set to work.

Chihun reported the state of affairs to the planter, who came out with a dog-whip and cracked it furiously. Moti Guj paid the white man the compliment of charging him nearly a quarter of a mile across the clearing and 'Hrrumphing' him into the verandah. Then he stood outside the house chuckling to himself, and shaking all over with the fun of it, as an elephant will.

'We'll thrash him,' said the planter. 'He shall have the finest thrashing that ever elephant received. Give Kala Nag and Nazim twelve foot of chain apiece, and tell them to lay on twenty blows.'

Kala Nag—which means Black Snake—and Nazim were two of the biggest elephants in the lines, and one of their duties was to administer the graver punishments, since no man can beat an elephant properly.

They took the whipping-chains and rattled them in their trunks as they sidled up to Moti Guj, meaning to hustle him between them. Moti Guj had never, in all his life of thirty-nine years, been whipped, and he did not intend to open new experiences. So he waited, weaving his head from right to left, and measuring the precise spot in Kala Nag's fat side where a blunt tusk would sink deepest. Kala Nag had no tusks; the chain was his badge of authority; but he judged it good to swing wide of Moti Guj at the last minute, and seem to appear as if he had brought out the chain for amusement. Nazim turned round and went home early. He did not feel fighting-fit that morning, and so Moti Guj was left standing alone with his ears cocked.

That decided the planter to argue no more, and Moti Guj rolled back to his inspection of the clearing. An elephant who will not work, and is not tied up, is not quite so manageable as an eighty-one ton gun loose in a heavy sea-way. He slapped old friends on the back and asked them if the stumps were coming away easily; he talked nonsense concerning labour and the inalienable rights of elephants to a long 'nooning'; and wandering to and fro, thoroughly demoralised the garden until sundown, when he returned to his pickets for food.

'If you won't work you shan't eat,' said Chihun angrily. 'You're a wild elephant, and no educated animal at all. Go back to your jungle.'

Chihun's little brown baby, rolling on the floor of the hut, stretched its fat arms to the huge shadow in the doorway. Moti Guj knew well that it was the dearest thing on earth to Chihun. He swung out his trunk with a fascinating crook at the end, and the brown baby threw itself shouting upon it. Moti Guj made fast and pulled up till the brown baby was crowing in the air twelve feet above his father's head.

'Great Chief!' said Chihun. 'Flour cakes of the best, twelve in number, two feet across, and soaked in rum shall be yours on the instant, and two hundred pounds' weight of fresh-cut young sugar-cane therewith. Deign only to put down safely that insignificant brat who is my heart and my life to me.'

Moti Guj tucked the brown baby comfortably between his forefeet, that could have knocked into toothpicks all Chihun's hut, and waited for his food. He ate it, and the brown baby crawled away. Moti Guj dozed, and thought of Deesa. One of many mysteries connected with the elephant is that his huge body needs less sleep than anything else that lives. Four or five hours in the night suffice —two just before midnight, lying down on one side; two just after one o'clock, lying down on the other. The rest of the silent hours are filled with eating and fidgeting and long grumbling soliloquies.

At midnight, therefore, Moti Guj strode out of his pickets, for a thought had come to him that Deesa might be lying drunk somewhere in the dark forest with none to look after him. So all that night he chased through the undergrowth, blowing and trumpeting and shaking his ears. He went down to the river and blared across the shallows where Deesa used to wash him, but there was no answer. He could not find Deesa, but he disturbed all the elephants in the lines, and nearly frightened to death some gipsies in the woods.

At dawn Deesa returned to the plantation. He had been very drunk indeed, and he expected to fall into trouble for outstaying his leave. He drew a long breath when he saw that the bungalow and the plantation were still uninjured; for he knew something of Moti Guj's temper; and reported himself with many lies and salaams. Moti Guj had gone to his pickets for breakfast. His night exercise had made him hungry.

'Call up your beast,' said the planter, and Deesa shouted in the mysterious elephant-language, that some mahouts believe came from China at the birth of the world, when elephants and not men were masters. Moti Guj heard and came. Elephants do not gallop. They move from spots at varying rates of speed. If an elephant wished to catch an express train he could not gallop, but he could catch the train. Thus Moti Guj was at the planter's door almost before Chihun noticed that he had left his pickets. He fell into Deesa's arms trumpeting with joy, and the man and beast wept and slobbered over each other, and handled each other from head to heel to see that no harm had befallen.

'Now we will get to work,' said Deesa. 'Lift me up, my son and my joy.'

Moti Guj swung him up and the two went to the coffee-clearing to look for irksome stumps.

The planter was too astonished to be very angry.

POETRY

THE NATIVE-BORN

We've drunk to the Queen—God bless her!—
We've drunk to our mothers' land;
We've drunk to our English brother
(But he does not understand);
We've drunk to the wide creation,
And the Cross swings low for the morn;
Last toast, and of obligation,
A health to the Native-born!

They change their skies above them,
But not their hearts that roam!
We learned from our wistful mothers
To call old England 'home';
We read of the English skylark,
Of the spring in the English lanes,
But we screamed with the painted lories
As we rode on the dusty plains!

They passed with their old-world legends—
Their tales of wrong and dearth—
Our fathers held by purchase,
But we by the right of birth;

Our heart's where they rocked our cradle,
Our love where we spent our toil,
And our faith and our hope and our honour
We pledge to our native soil!

I charge you charge your glasses—
I charge you drink with me
To the men of the Four New Nations,
And the Islands of the Sea—
To the last least lump of coral
That none may stand outside,
And our own good pride shall teach us
To praise our comrade's pride!

To the hush of the breathless morning
On the thin, tin, crackling roofs,
To the haze of the burned back-ranges
And the dust of the shoeless hoofs—
To the risk of a death by drowning,
To the risk of a death by drouth—
To the men of a million acres,
To the Sons of the Golden South!

To the Sons of the Golden South (Stand up!),
And the life we live and know,
Let a fellow sing o' the little things he cares about,
If a fellow fights for the little things he cares about
With the weight of a single blow!

To the smoke of a hundred coasters,
To the sheep on a thousand hills,
To the sun that never blisters,
To the rain that never chills—
To the land of the waiting spring-time,
To our five-meal, meat-fed men,

To the tall, deep-bosomed women,
  And the children nine and ten!

And the children nine and ten (Stand up!),
  And the life we live and know,
Let a fellow sing o' the little things he cares about,
If a fellow fights for the little things he cares about
  With the weight of a two-fold blow!

To the far-flung fenceless prairie
  Where the quick cloud-shadows trail,
To our neighbour's barn in the offing
  And the line of the new-cut rail;
To the plough in her league-long furrow
  With the gray Lake gulls behind—
To the weight of a half-year's winter
  And the warm wet western wind!

To the home of the floods and thunder,
  To her pale dry healing blue—
To the lift of the great Cape combers,
  And the smell of the baked Karroo.
To the growl of the sluicing stamp-head—
  To the reef and the water-gold,
To the last and the largest Empire,
  To the map that is half unrolled!

To our dear dark foster-mothers,
  To the heathen songs they sung—
To the heathen speech we babbled
  Ere we came to the white man's tongue.
To the cool of our deep verandas—
  To the blaze of our jewelled main,
To the night, to the palms in the moonlight,
  And the fire-fly in the cane!

To the hearth of our people's people—
To her well-ploughed windy sea,
To the hush of our dread high-altar
Where The Abbey makes us We;
To the grist of the slow-ground ages,
To the gain that is yours and mine—
To the Bank of the Open Credit,
To the Power-house of the Line!

We've drunk to the Queen—God bless her!—
We've drunk to our mothers' land;
We've drunk to our English brother
(And we hope he'll understand).
We've drunk as much as we're able,
And the Cross swings low for the morn;
Last toast—and your foot on the table!—
A health to the Native-born!

A health to the Native-born (Stand up!),
We're six white men arow,
All bound to sing o' the little things we care about,
All bound to fight for the little things we care about
With the weight of a six-fold blow!
By the might of our cable-tow (Take hands!),
From the Orkneys to the Horn,
All round the world (and a little loop to pull it by),
All round the world (and a little strap to buckle it),
A health to the Native-born!

THE FLOWERS

To our private taste, there is always something a little exotic, almost artificial, in songs which, under an English aspect and dress, are yet so manifestly the product of other skies. They affect us like translations; the very fauna and flora are alien, remote; the dog's-tooth violet is but an ill substitute for the rathe primrose, nor can we ever believe that the wood-robin sings as sweetly in April as the English thrush.—THE ATHENÆUM.

Buy my English posies!
Kent and Surrey may—
Violets of the Undercliff
Wet with Channel spray;
Cowslips from a Devon combe—
Midland furze afire—
Buy my English posies
And I'll sell your heart's desire!

Buy my English posies!
You that scorn the May,
Won't you greet a friend from home
Half the world away?
Green against the draggled drift,
Faint and frail and first—
Buy my Northern blood-root
And I'll know where you were nursed:

Robin down the logging-road whistles, 'Come to me!'
Spring has found the maple-grove, the sap is running free;
All the winds of Canada call the ploughing-rain.
Take the flower and turn the hour, and kiss your love again!

Buy my English posies!
  Here's to match your need—
Buy a tuft of royal heath,
  Buy a bunch of weed
White as sand of Muysenberg
  Spun before the gale—
Buy my heath and lilies
  And I'll tell you whence you hail!
Under hot Constantia broad the vineyards lie—
Throned and thorned the aching berg props the speckless
    sky—
Slow below the Wynberg firs trails the tilted wain—
Take the flower and turn the hour, and kiss your love again!

Buy my English posies!
  You that will not turn—
Buy my hot-wood clematis,
  Buy a frond o' fern
Gathered where the Erskine leaps
  Down the road to Lorne—
Buy my Christmas creeper
  And I'll say where you were born!
West away from Melbourne dust holidays begin—
They that mock at Paradise woo at Cora Lynn—
Through the great South Otway gums sings the great South
    Main—
Take the flower and turn the hour, and kiss your love again!

Buy my English posies!
  Here's your choice unsold!

Buy a blood-red myrtle-bloom,
Buy the kowhai's gold
Flung for gift on Taupo's face,
Sign that spring is come—
Buy my clinging myrtle
And I'll give you back your home!
Broom behind the windy town; pollen o' the pine—
Bell-bird in the leafy deep where the *ratas* twine—
Fern above the saddle-bow, flax upon the plain—
Take the flower and turn the hour, and kiss your love again!

Buy my English posies!
Ye that have your own,
Buy them for a brother's sake
Overseas, alone.
Weed ye trample underfoot
Floods his heart abrim—
Bird ye never heeded,
Oh, she calls his dead to him!
Far and far our homes are set round the Seven Seas;
Woe for us if we forget, we that hold by these!
Unto each his mother-beach, bloom and bird and land—
Masters of the Seven Seas, oh, love and understand.

MUNICIPAL.

"Why is my District death-rate low?"
Said Binks of Hezabad
"Wells, drains, and sewage-outfalls are
"My own peculiar fad.
"I learnt a lesson once. It ran
"Thus," quoth that most veracious man:—

It was an August evening and, in snowy garments clad,
I paid a round of visits in the lines of Hezabad;
When, presently, my Waler saw, and did not like at all,
A Commissariat elephant careering down the Mall.

I couldn't see the driver, and across my mind it rushed
That that Commissariat elephant had suddenly gone *musth*.
I didn't care to meet him, and I couldn't well get down,
So I let the Waler have it, and we headed for the town.

The buggy was a new one and, praise Dykes, it stood the strain,
Till the Waler jumped a bullock just above the City Drain;
And the next that I remember was a hurricane of squeals,
And the creature making toothpicks of my five-foot patent wheels.

He seemed to want the owner, so I fled, distraught with fear,
To the Main Drain sewage outfall while he snorted in my ear—

Reached the four-foot drain-head safely and, in darkness and despair,
Felt the brute's proboscis fingering my terror-stiffened hair,

Heard it trumpet on my shoulder—tried to crawl a little higher—
Found the Main Drain sewage-outfall blocked some eight feet up, with mire;
And, for twenty reeking minutes, Sir, my very marrow froze,
While the trunk was feeling blindly for a purchase on my toes!

It missed me by a fraction, but my hair was turning grey
Before they called the drivers up and dragged the brute away.
Then I sought the City Elders, and my words were very plain.
They flushed that four-foot drain-head and—it never choked again.

You may hold with surface-drainage, and the sun-for-garbage cure,
Till you've been a periwinkle shrinking coyly up a sewer.
I believe in well-flushed culverts. . . .
This is why the death-rate's small;
And, if you don't believe me, get *shikarred* yourself. That's all.

THE COASTWISE LIGHTS

OUR brows are bound with spindrift and the weed is on our knees;
Our loins are battered 'neath us by the swinging, smoking seas.
From reef and rock and skerry—over headland, ness, and voe—
The Coastwise Lights of England watch the ships of England go!

Through the endless summer evenings, on the lineless, level floors;
Through the yelling Channel tempest when the siren hoots and roars—
By day the dipping house-flag and by night the rocket's trail—
As the sheep that graze behind us so we know them where they hail.

We bridge across the dark, and bid the helmsman have a care,
The flash that wheeling inland wakes his sleeping wife to prayer;

From our vexed eyries, head to gale, we bind in burning
chains
The lover from the sea-rim drawn—his love in English
lanes.

We greet the clippers wing-and-wing that race the Southern
wool;
We warn the crawling cargo tanks of Bremen, Leith, and
Hull;
To each and all our equal lamp at peril of the sea—
The white wall-sided war-ships or the whalers of Dundee!

Come up, come in from Eastward, from the guard-ports of
the Morn!
Beat up, beat in from Southerly, O gipsies of the Horn!
Swift shuttles of an Empire's loom that weave us, main to
main,
The Coastwise Lights of England give you welcome back
again!

Go, get you gone up-Channel with the sea-crust on your
plates;
Go, get you into London with the burden of your freights!
Haste, for they talk of Empire there, and say, if any seek,
The Lights of England sent you and by silence shall ye
speak.

THE ENGLISH FLAG

Above the portico a flag-staff, bearing the Union Jack, remained fluttering in the flames for some time, but ultimately when it fell the crowds rent the air with shouts, and seemed to see significance in the incident.—DAILY PAPERS.

WINDS of the World, give answer! They are whimpering to and fro—
And what should they know of England who only England know?—
The poor little street-bred people that vapour and fume and brag,
They are lifting their heads in the stillness to yelp at the English Flag!

Must we borrow a clout from the Boer—to plaster anew with dirt?
An Irish liar's bandage, or an English coward's shirt?
We may not speak of England; her Flag's to sell or share.
What is the Flag of England? Winds of the World, declare!

The North Wind blew:—'From Bergen my steel-shod vanguards go;
I chase your lazy whalers home from the Disko floe;
By the great North Lights above me I work the will of God,
And the liner splits on the ice-field or the Dogger fills with cod.

'I barred my gates with iron, I shuttered my doors with flame,
Because to force my ramparts your nutshell navies came;
I took the sun from their presence, I cut them down with my blast,
And they died, but the Flag of England blew free ere the spirit passed.

'The lean white bear hath seen it in the long, long Arctic night,
The musk-ox knows the standard that flouts the Northern Light:
What is the Flag of England? Ye have but my bergs to dare,
Ye have but my drifts to conquer. Go forth, for it is there!'

The South Wind sighed:—'From the Virgins my mid-sea course was ta'en
Over a thousand islands lost in an idle main,
Where the sea-egg flames on the coral and the long-backed breakers croon
Their endless ocean legends to the lazy, locked lagoon.

'Strayed amid lonely islets, mazed amid outer keys,
I waked the palms to laughter—I tossed the scud in the breeze—
Never was isle so little, never was sea so lone,
But over the scud and the palm-trees an English flag was flown.

'I have wrenched it free from the halliard to hang for a wisp on the Horn;
I have chased it north to the Lizard—ribboned and rolled and torn;

I have spread its fold o'er the dying, adrift in a hopeless sea;
I have hurled it swift on the slaver, and seen the slave set free.

'My basking sunfish know it, and wheeling albatross,
Where the lone wave fills with fire beneath the Southern Cross.
What is the Flag of England? Ye have but my reefs to dare,
Ye have but my seas to furrow. Go forth, for it is there!

The East Wind roared:—'From the Kuriles, the Bitter Seas, I come,
And me men call the Home-Wind, for I bring the English home.
Look—look well to your shipping! By the breath of my mad typhoon
I swept your close-packed Praya and beached your best at Kowloon!

'The reeling junks behind me and the racing seas before,
I raped your richest roadstead—I plundered Singapore!
I set my hand on the Hoogli; as a hooded snake she rose,
And I flung your stoutest steamers to roost with the startled crows.

'Never the lotus closes, never the wild-fowl wake,
But a soul goes out on the East Wind that died for England's sake—
Man or woman or suckling, mother or bride or maid—
Because on the bones of the English the English Flag is stayed.

'The desert-dust hath dimmed it, the flying wild-ass knows,
The scared white leopard winds it across the taintless snows

What is the Flag of England? Ye have but my sun to
dare,
Ye have but my sands to travel. Go forth, for it is there!'

The West Wind called:—'In squadrons the thoughtless
galleons fly
That bear the wheat and cattle lest street-bred people die.
They make my might their porter, they make my house
their path,
Till I loose my neck from their rudder and whelm them all
in my wrath.

'I draw the gliding fog-bank as a snake is drawn from the
hole,
They bellow one to the other, the frighted ship-bells toll,
For day is a drifting terror till I raise the shroud with my
breath,
And they see strange bows above them and the two go
locked to death.

'But whether in calm or wrack-wreath, whether by dark or
day,
I heave them whole to the conger or rip their plates away,
First of the scattered legions, under a shrieking sky,
Dipping between the rollers, the English Flag goes by.

'The dead dumb fog hath wrapped it—the frozen dews have
kissed—
The naked stars have seen it, the fellow-star in the mist.
What is the Flag of England? Ye have but my breath to
dare,
Ye have but my waves to conquer. Go forth, for it is
there!'

ENGLAND'S ANSWER

Truly ye come of The Blood; slower to bless than to ban;
Little used to lie down at the bidding of any man.
Flesh of the flesh that I bred, bone of the bone that I bare;
Stark as your sons shall be—stern as your fathers were.
Deeper than speech our love, stronger than life our tether,
But we do not fall on the neck nor kiss when we come
together.
My arm is nothing weak, my strength is not gone by;
Sons, I have borne many sons, but my breasts are not dry,
Look, I have made ye a place and opened wide the doors,
That ye may talk together, your Barons and Councillors—
Wards of the Outer March, Lords of the Lower Seas,
Ay, talk to your gray mother that bore you on her knees!—
That ye may talk together, brother to brother's face—
Thus for the good of your peoples—thus for the Pride of
the Race.
Also, we will make promise. So long as The Blood endures,
I shall know that your good is mine: ye shall feel that my
strength is yours:
In the day of Armageddon, at the last great fight of all,
That Our House stand together and the pillars do not fall.
Draw now the threefold knot firm on the ninefold bands,
And the Law that ye make shall be law after the rule of
your lands.
This for the waxen Heath, and that for the Wattle-bloom,
This for the Maple-leaf, and that for the southern Broom.

The Law that ye make shall be law and I do not press my
will,
Because ye are Sons of The Blood and call me Mother still.
Now must ye speak to your kinsmen and they must speak
to you,
After the use of the English, in straight-flung words and
few.
Go to your work and be strong, halting not in your ways,
Balking the end half-won for an instant dole of praise.
Stand to your work and be wise—certain of sword and pen,
Who are neither children nor Gods, but men in a world of
men!

THE OVERLAND MAIL

[Foot-service to the Hills]

In the name of the Empress of India, make way,
  O Lords of the Jungle, wherever you roam,
The woods are astir at the close of the day—
  We exiles are waiting for letters from Home.
Let the robber retreat—let the tiger turn tail—
In the Name of the Empress, the Overland Mail!

With a jingle of bells as the dusk gathers in,
  He turns to the foot-path that heads up the hill—
The bags on his back and a cloth round his chin,
  And, tucked in his waistbelt, the Post Office bill;—
'Despatched on this date, as received by the rail,
'*Per* runner, two bags of the Overland Mail.'

Is the torrent in spate? He must ford it or swim.
  Has the rain wrecked the road? He must climb by the
    cliff.
Does the tempest cry 'halt'? What are tempests to him?
  The service admits not a 'but' or an 'if.'

While the breath's in his mouth, he must bear without fail,
In the Name of the Empress, the Overland Mail.

From aloe to rose-oak, from rose-oak to fir,
  From level to upland, from upland to crest,
From rice-field to rock-ridge, from rock-ridge to spur,
  Fly the soft-sandalled feet, strains the brawny brown
    chest.
From rail to ravine—to the peak from the vale—
Up, up through the night goes the Overland Mail.

There's a speck on the hill-side, a dot on the road—
  A jingle of bells on the foot-path below—
There's a scuffle above in the monkey's abode—
  The world is awake and the clouds are aglow.
For the great Sun himself must attend to the hail :—
'In the Name of the Empress, the Overland Mail!'

IN SPRING TIME

My garden blazes brightly with the rose-bush and the
peach,
And the *köil* sings above it, in the *siris* by the well,
From the creeper-covered trellis comes the squirrel's
chattering speech,
And the blue jay screams and flutters where the cheery
satbhai dwell.
But the rose has lost its fragrance, and the *köil's* note is
strange;
I am sick of endless sunshine, sick of blossom-burdened
bough.
Give me back the leafless woodlands where the winds of
Springtime range—
Give me back one day in England, for it's Spring in
England now!
Through the pines the gusts are booming, o'er the brown
fields blowing chill,
From the furrow of the plough-share streams the
fragrance of the loam,
And the hawk nests on the cliffside and the jackdaw in the
hill,
And my heart is back in England 'mid the sights and
sounds of Home.
But the garland of the sacrifice this wealth of rose and
peach is,
Ah! *köil*, little *köil*, singing on the *siris* bough,
In my ears the knell of exile your ceaseless bell-like speech
is—
Can *you* tell me aught of England or of Spring in
England now?

PRINTED IN GREAT BRITAIN BY ROBERT MACLEHOSE AND CO. LTD.
THE UNIVERSITY PRESS, GLASGOW.

Westward Ho! By Charles Kingsley. Abridged Edition for Schools. With Illustrations. 2s.

Tom Brown's School Days. By T. Hughes. Abridged Edition for Schools. Illustrated. 2s.

The Kipling Reader. Selected from the Works of Rudyard Kipling for use in Schools. 2s. 6d.

The Talisman. By Sir W. Scott. Abridged Edition for Schools. Illustrated. 2s.

Ivanhoe. By Sir W. Scott. Abridged Edition for Schools. Illustrated. 2s.

Kenilworth. By Sir W. Scott. Abridged Edition for Schools. Illustrated. 2s.

Quentin Durward. By Sir W. Scott. Abridged Edition for Schools. Illus. 2s.

Rob Roy. By Sir W. Scott. Abridged Edition for Schools. Illustrated. 2s.

Our Sea Power. By H. W. Household. Illustrated. 2s.

The Lances of Lynwood. By C. M. Yonge. Abridged Edition for Schools. Illustrated. 2s. Complete, 2s. 6d. net.

Nellie's Memories. By Rosa N. Carey. Abridged Edition for Schools. 1s. 6d.

The Man-Eaters of Tsavo. By Lieut.-Colonel J. H. Patterson. Illustrated. Abridged Edition for Schools. 2s. Complete, 2s. net.

The Jungle Book. "The School Kipling." Illustrated. 4s.

The Second Jungle Book. "The School Kipling." Illustrated. 4s.

Puck of Pook's Hill. "The School Kipling." Illustrated. 4s.

Rewards and Fairies. "The School Kipling." Illustrated. 4s.

Captains Courageous. "The School Kipling." Illustrated. 4s.

Just So Stories. "The School Kipling." Illustrated. 4s.

Aly the Philosopher and other Stories. By W. Swithin Roberts. With coloured Illustrations by H. R. Millar. 2s.

Hands and Feet. By W. Swithin Roberts. Illustrated by H. R. Millar. 2s.

The Adventures of Ulysses. By W. H. D. Rouse, Litt.D. 2s. 6d.

Stories of the Old Greeks. By W. H. D. Rouse, Litt.D. 2s.

To the Forbidden Land: Discoveries and Adventures in Tibet, Selected and Adapted from Sven Hedin's *Trans-Himalaya.* Illustrated. 1s. 9d.

Greeks and Romans. By W. F. Houghton. Illustrated. 2s.

The Story of a Red-Deer. By Sir John Fortescue. 2s. 6d. net.

The Little Duke. By Charlotte M. Yonge. 2s. net.

The Dove in the Eagle's Nest. By Charlotte M. Yonge. 2s. net.

The Chaplet of Pearls. By Charlotte M. Yonge. 2s. 6d. net.

The Prince and the Page. By Charlotte M. Yonge. 2s. 6d. net.

The Youngest Girl in the School. By Evelyn Sharp. 2s. net.

Action and Adventure. Edited by N. B. McKellar, M.A. 2s.

The Rose and the Ring. By W. M. Thackeray. 2s. net.

MACMILLAN & CO., LTD., LONDON